BUILDING THE BRIL

LILLIAN KING

WINDFALL BOOKS

ISBN NO: 0 9539839 7 8

ACKNOWLEDGEMENTS

For Belle, who was always there for me

In May 1999, Fife Fringe organised an exhibition in Kirkcaldy Museum & Art Gallery.
The core of that exhibition was a series of pictures by Morris Allan charting the building of the Forth Road
Bridge between 1957 and 1964. It was decided that the fortieth anniversary of the Bridge's opening
was an ideal time to reprise and extend this display of Morris' pictures.
This book has been designed to commemorate the anniversary and to pay tribute to the work of
Morris Allan and other photographers who recorded the history of the bridge.

I would like to express my gratitude to all the people who helped in the compilation of this book.
Special thanks go to:
Morris Allan, who was the inspiration for the whole project
Alastair Andrew, Forth Bridge Master and his staff for their invaluable assistance,
and for the use of archive photographs
Andrew Neil, Arts Policy Co-ordinator, Fife Council
Chris Neale, Fife Council Libraries
Talisman Films

THIS PROJECT WAS FUNDED BY THE HERITAGE LOTTERY

© Lillian King September 2004
Cover design by Belle Hammond/Artwork by Morris Allan
Printed by Nevisprint, Fort William
Typesetting, layout and design by Windfall Books
Published by Windfall Books

FOREWORD

The Forth Bridge, opened in 1890 saw the first use of steel in a large structure and beside it the slender Forth Road Bridge opened in 1964. In its day, it was the longest span suspension bridge outside America.

Lillian's carefully researched book covers the history of the planning and construction of the Road Bridge and attempts to look into the future, suggesting that history may be repeated. This is the time to have an informed debate on the case for another bridge as the traffic weight and density continues to grow well above the design load case for the existing structure.

The staff at the bridge will continue to endeavour to maintain the bridge to a high standard but these works will by necessity progressively impinge on the service level afforded to bridge users as traffic increases and the bridge grows older.

I have enjoyed assisting Lillian in a small way in preparing the book and I commend it to anyone at all interested in the history of the bridge and its construction.

Alastair Andrew BSc. C.Eng. M.I.C.E.
General Manager and Bridgemaster
Forth Estuary Transport Authority.

July 2004.

Good, dependable transport links are vital to the social and economic well being of a country and nowhere is this truer than in the case of long span bridges spanning tidal waters. Here at Queensferry we can see two world class examples of pioneering civil/structural engineering at its best.

A naval vessel makes its way under the Forth Rail Bridge

IN THE BEGINNING

When the Queen opened the new Road over the Forth on September 4th, 1964, she unveiled a plaque which marked the end of at least eight centuries of royal involvement in the history of the river.

A pilgrim route to St Andrews existed long before the eleventh century when, during the reign of Malcolm Canmore, Queen Margaret granted free passage by her new ferry to those on pilgrimage. A regular ferry service across the Forth was instituted about the year 1130, and in 1164 Malcolm IV granted a charter naming the crossing *Passagium Regina*, the Queen's passage, though the first official record of the name does not appear until 1184.

In 1275, the Abbot of Dunfermline Abbey, which owned the ferry, set up 'eight oars in the new passage boats' and two of these were allotted to women. Alexander III is thought to have crossed the Forth, hurrying home to his new young wife, on the night of his death at Kinghorn in 1286.

Robert I had a landing point at North Queensferry and a chapel there was dedicated by him to Dunfermline Abbey in 1320. The priors and canons of the Abbey were granted free passage with their men and goods. Robert retained what were known as the hospital lands, where hospitia or shelters for pilgrims had been built.

James I ordered gang planks to be used to facilitate the loading and unloading of animals. Mary of Guise travelled south From North Queensferry after her marriage to James V in St Andrews. Her daughter, Mary Queen of Scots used the ferry regularly, once after her escape from prison in Loch Leven Castle. By the time Mary's son, James VI, came to the throne, ferry boats were big enough to carry eighty people.

After the Reformation, Dunfermline Abbey and its lands and wealth became the property of the monarch, and was run by a lay commendator. The ferry belonged to the Abbey and had therefore been inherited by James, who presented it to his wife, Anne of Denmark, as a wedding gift.

The ferry played an important role in both peace and war. James' grandson, Charles II visited North Queensferry and Inchgarvie to inspect the garrisons built to prevent Cromwell's troops from passing over the Forth. By 1669, there were four boats in service and official instructions given for use insisted on no Sunday service except in times of severe sickness or 'public concernment.' Fifty years later, numbers had doubled, all boats were kept on the north shore and all the boatmen had to come from North Queensferry.

Sometimes boats sank or were swept downstream and wrecked and losses were blamed on greed rather than carelessness on the part of the boatmen. The ferry was closed on several occasions in war times, to prevent men from the north joining southern troops, and to stop soldiers who wanted to return home after battles. At least twice, it was officially closed to prevent the spread of plague, but ferrymen were their own masters and if someone wanted to cross, they were ready to oblige. No-one paid any attention to the ban, therefore, and commissioners were sent to strip the sails from the masts of boats to prevent them sailing, in an attempt to stop the disease spreading.

Over the years, improvements to ship design added to the comfort and safety of passengers, but until the advent of steam powered ships early in the nineteenth century, ferries were entirely dependent on wind and tides. From the ferry's earliest days, arrival and departure points on both sides of the river were based on natural rock landfalls but, by 1710, man made structures were in place. Conditions on these were poor and, at times, dangerous.

Two factors hastened the speed of improvements: the Industrial Revolution with its development of trade and communications, and the building of military roads in the north of Scotland following the Jacobite Rebellions. The Forfeited Estates Commissioners contributed money to the improvements needed because the ferry was seen as an integral part of that military road system, as well as the most frequented sea passage in Scotland.

By 1807, local landowners, including William Adam of Blairadam, were arguing the need for the ferry to be taken into public ownership, and administered by trustees, because it was an important part of the Great North Road. This was agreed and, as a result, new harbours and piers were designed and built by the best engineers of the day.

John Smeaton, who had engineered the Forth and Clyde Canal, and built bridges at Perth and Coldstream, suggested that several landing places on each side of the river should be established and extensions made to existing piers.

Two new landings on each shore served reasonably well for the next twenty years until further improvements were carried out by John Rennie. He had been involved in bridge, harbour and lighthouse building so was well qualified for the task.

He carried out Smeaton's suggestion for several landing places and built a pier to be used for loading and unloading cattle. Another engineer, Robert Stephenson of Bell Rock fame, was called on by the ferry supervisor to advise about lighting arrangements when a new lighthouse was built.

A report for the year ending 15th May, 1811, gives an idea of the volume of traffic carried: over eighty three thousand people, nearly six thousand carriages and carts, and over forty four thousand animals. Eight boats carried between them four hundred and fifty people per day, as well as stage coaches to and from Edinburgh, Aberdeen and Perth.

Ten years later, the *Queen Margaret*, a steam powered paddle boat was brought into service but could only cope with foot passengers. Because of the paddles, wheeled traffic could not be transferred from pier to ship.

A new ferry between Newhaven and Dysart had begun in 1819, but the *Queen Margaret* couldn't cope with the competition., and very soon passengers deserted the Queensferry passage for a more efficient service.

A number of improvements had to be made, including extending piers, building breakwaters and making deeper anchorages, before steam ships could be used between North and South Queensferry. By 1821, a fleet of sailing ships had been introduced but it was obvious that steam would play an increasingly dominant role in the future.

Thomas Telford, the famous engineer and bridge builder, was called upon to give advice about changing the system from sailing ships to steam powered craft.

He did not think that the estimated income would justify expensive improvements, but suggested pier extensions and the building of breakwaters. Improvements to the new steam ferries between Fife and Granton, however, were considered worth investing in.

After the rail bridge was built, the ferry became a shadow of its former self, regular runs being supplemented by sight seeing trips. In the 1920s, the North British Railway Company took over control of the ferry, with three boats in service.

Already the carriages and carts of previous year were being replaced by cars, and the *Dundee* could carry nine hundred and ninety seven passengers but only ten cars, so two new ships were commissioned. The

Even with three boats, the ferry company couldn't begin to cope with the increase in traffic

Queen Margaret and the *Robert the Bruce* were launched in 1934, carrying twenty eight cars and running a half hour service.

The *Mary, Queen of Scots* began carrying passengers in 1949, and a fifteen minute service was started. But even this was not enough for an ever increasing stream of cars and commuters, and it was becoming increasingly obvious that an alternative means of crossing the river would have to be found.

By the time the new road bridge was finished in 1964, the ferry was having to cope with two million passengers and nine hundred thousand cars, and this was still not enough.

For many years, various attempts had been made to find an alternative means of crossing the river. *The History of The Forth Bridge*, published in 1911 claimed that as early as 1740, a proposal for a tunnel between North and South Queensferry was under consideration, but offered no details.

It was a feasible suggestion, because a tunnel under the Forth had been built more than a hundred years earlier by Sir George Bruce of Carnock. A coffer dam, a circular frame of stones, joined together with bituminous matter was built at low tide, and miners dug down over two hundred feet to find coal.

The tunnel, which was visited by James VI in 1617, stretched more than a mile under the sea and was described as being cut as an arch or vault and big enough for a man to walk upright in most places. Legend has it that, hearing voices from the other end of the tunnel, James cried 'Treason,' thinking he had been led into an ambush, and was only partly mollified when assured that it was only Sir George's miners.

The success of George Bruce's venture was followed by under sea coal workings at Bo'ness and Whitehaven at depths of from five to nine hundred feet, but it was not till 1805 that another plan for a Forth tunnel was put forward. Mining experts of the day were consulted and a report in 1807 suggested a tunnel with fifteen feet wide carriageways and two footpaths, the north entrance to be near Rosyth Castle, the south at Abercorn.

The estimated cost was around £164,000, a prospectus was drawn up and shares offered at £100 each, but the project foundered through lack of support. This was probably just as well. The plan was seriously flawed, because the designers worked on a false assumption.

They assumed that tunnelling would be through a band of freestone extending from shore to shore, at a depth of a hundred and eighty feet. They were proved correct about the rock formation in 1964, when the Kinneil and Valleyfield mines were joined by a tunnel under the Forth, but it was at a depth of eighteen hundred feet. If the earlier project had gone ahead, the engineers would have encountered a deep channel in the bed of the river, filled with sand and silt.

Until the Industrial Revolution, the only materials for bridge building would have been wood and stone, neither of them suitable for building in deep water. It was not till the production of uniformly good quality wrought iron, that engineers could seriously consider the possibility of constructing metal suspension bridges.

The first feasible plan, for a bridge crossing the Forth, designed by Edinburgh civil engineer and land surveyor James Anderson, appeared in 1817. Aware of Thomas Telford's plans for a similar bridge across the Mersey, he produced comparatively detailed documentation for the construction of a chain bridge. It would be, he claimed, *'the work of greatest utility, of the first national and commercial advantage – it would prevent mails from being interrupted, preserve the passage from the hazards of the ferry, and serve military requirements etc.'*

This bridge, which would take four years to build, was to be situated four hundred yards east of Newhalls Inn and would be supported on Inchgarvie Island, touching Fife on the Battery Rock at North Queensferry.

It would rise ninety to one hundred and ten feet above spring tides to preserve steam navigation and allow vessels of up to four hundred tons to pass through with the top gallant masts up. Supporting chains were to be fixed to iron towers and it was calculated that these could bear up to one hundred and twenty tons.

Anderson's plans included three spans, either one twenty five foot wide roadway with four foot wide platforms on either side or two thirteen and a half feet carriageways and one six foot wide pathway. The roadways would be oak planks, either with iron studs or covered with pitch, and the parapet a cast iron baluster six feet high lined with sheet iron. Loaded wagons would take twenty five minutes to cross and a gentleman's carriage eight to ten minutes.

North Queensferry pier and approach roads

Unfortunately, this plan too failed to find sufficient support and it was to be another hundred years before a successful scheme was launched.

With the advent of the railway age a proposal for a rail bridge was put forward by the North British Railway Company in 1860. It did not materialise, but by 1873 a design by Thomas Bouch was adopted by the Forth Bridge Company and work had actually begun when the Tay Bridge disaster on 29 December, 1879 led to its abandonment.

The rail bridge was at last achieved by the famous cantilever structure designed by John Fowler and Benjamin Baker and built by Tancred, Arrol and Co. Ltd. It was opened by H.R.H. The Prince of Wales on 4 March, 1890.

To help pay the cost of the bridge, a special surcharge was levied through railway freight and passenger charges.

The rail link reduced the clamour for a road crossing, but by the 1920s the enormous increase in traffic brought renewed demands. By then, local authorities on both sides of the river recognised the need for a road link across the River Forth, encouraged by the general belief that a road bridge would help to advance the development of Scotland's coal fields. It was confidently predicted that coal stocks would last four or five hundred years.

In November 1923, James Inglis Ker, a leading campaigner for a road bridge until his death in 1936, put forward his proposal for a bridge, at a press conference held at the Hawes Inn, South Queensferry.

He wrote that:

The building of a road bridge across the Forth is admittedly a proposition of the first magnitude and it is not to be lightly considered. It will tax the minds of our greatest road builders and bridge engineers, while in its financial aspects it will demand the most searching examination on the part of the Ministry of Transport and local authorities concerned. I think it will be generally conceded that there is an urgent need for such a bridge and that its advantages to the entire community would be incalculable.

There is no reason why Scotland, the cradle land of many eminent engineers, should be behind other countries in the new movement. It is the natural order of things that the country which gave the world its finest achievements in railway bridges should now lead the way in road bridge engineering.'

He believed that a road bridge was all that was required to restore Edinburgh to its rightful place as the gateway to the north, and that it would materially enhance the usefulness of the new highway between Glasgow, Edinburgh, and Leith.

A bridge would bring these three centres into direct contact with Dunfermline, Kirkcaldy, Perth, and Dundee, provide employment for five thousand men who could be accommodated at Rosyth and would stimulate the steel, iron, wood, cement, brick, stone, and lime industries.

The estimated construction period would be approximately five years. His design was for a suspension bridge which would be constructed east of the railway bridge and would feature two spans, each 2400 feet, sharing a common pier on Inch Garvie.

Support for his plans came from Sir Henry Maybury, Director General of Roads and Bridges under the Ministry of Transport, who agreed that the bridge would be of immeasurable service to the rapidly increasing road traffic throughout the east of Scotland. On 18 January 1924 an informal gathering took place in Edinburgh, attended by members and officials from the local authorities of Edinburgh, Linlithgow, Dunfermline, South and North Queensferry, Inverkeithing, Perth, Kirkcaldy, and Dundee.

Also represented were motoring organisations and other interested parties. A Ministry of Transport representative told the delegates that the proposal was worthy of the most serious consideration, and that from an engineering point of view, the construction was not expected to present any difficulty.

The next meeting was held at the House of Commons on 25 March, and was attended by thirty Scottish MPs. After a full discussion, a committee was appointed to press the scheme on the Ministry of Transport, who offered to pay seventy five per cent of the cost of a survey, provided the balance was met by the local authorities.

A meeting of those authorities in the Forth area was then held in Edinburgh on 21 January 1925, to discuss the Government's offer, and though they agreed that the proposed bridge would form a link in a national highway, the authorities were of the opinion that the full cost of the preliminary survey, in the region of ten thousand pounds, should be borne by the State. Agreement was reached and in January 1926, Messrs Mott, Hay & Anderson were appointed to make a survey and report on a road bridge across the Forth at Queensferry.

Various locations were considered and bore hole investigations carried out on possible sites by Messrs John Cochrane & Sons Ltd of Westminster. The survey was completed in 1928 and preliminary reports were submitted to the Ministry of Transport the following year.

Three possible sites were investigated. Beamer Rock, a mile above the railway bridge, was the first site to be considered, but it was almost covered at high water, was not big enough at low tide to form a foundation for a large pier, and borings confirmed that a firm foundation could be found only at a very great depth. It was also in close proximity to the dredged channel leading to Rosyth Dockyard, and it was felt that this might be objected to by the Admiralty.

No borings were necessary on the second site, which was on the downstream side, and close to the railway bridge, for which records were already available, but this site was likely to be opposed by the railway company.

From an aesthetic viewpoint, the engineers considered that putting a new bridge alongside the railway bridge would be a great mistake. In addition, a suspension bridge in close proximity to the existing structure might result in serious difficulties with cross winds.

The third site, and the one considered the most suitable, was about one mile downstream from the railway bridge, in an area of comparatively shallow water on the south shore near Hound Point. Soundings near the north shore towards Inverkeithing appeared to indicate a submerged island, and boring at this site showed that solid rock was available but at rather great depths.

A suspension bridge with a centre span of 2400 feet was proposed, with provision for a forty foot wide roadway and two five foot wide pathways. A further report in 1930 gave more details of the scheme, but this plan, like others that had gone before, was destined to fail, because of the country's economic crisis which halted all bridge building.

Lack of money, however, did not mean a shortage of ideas. In 1931, another new scheme proposed a crossing about half way between the Beamer Rock site and the railway bridge. It would make use of the Mackintosh Rock, a submerged rock on the north side of the estuary, which was considered suitable for founding the pier of a large suspension bridge. The main span under this proposal was six hundred feet longer than the initial proposal.

In the same year, Sir Alexander Gibb & Partners were asked by the Ministry of Transport to examine the possibilities of erecting a bridge at what was known as the Hopetoun/Rosyth site, about a quarter of a mile upstream.

There were several things in favour of this: it was thought that Rosyth Naval Base might be used commercially; the arm of the dockyard would have reduced the overall length of the bridge; and approach roads were readily available. The price, however, proved prohibitive, the estimated cost of over six million pounds too great a sum to be acceptable, and the national economic crisis of the early thirties interrupted investigation for a time.

By 1934, however, it was possible to compare bridge costs at the Hopetoun/Rosyth and Mackintosh Rock sites. With thirty foot carriageways and two five foot pathways, the estimated cost of either bridge was between three and five million pounds.

Engineers under Sir David Anderson continued investigations, however, and another engineering report, this time using the Mackintosh rock as a pier support, was published.

Although there was general agreement that the project should go ahead, no government grants were available and it was again postponed. At the same time as investigations for the bridge were being carried out, others were going ahead for an altogether different crossing of the Forth in the vicinity of Kincardine, or at a site near Alloa.

Kincardine, some twenty seven miles west of Edinburgh and about ten miles nearer than the closest bridge over the Forth at Stirling was the more favourable location. A bridge at this site offered considerable benefits to traffic and the estimated cost, of what was, at the time, the largest swing bridge in the world, with a twenty foot wide carriageway and two footpaths each six feet wide, was three hundred and eleven thousand pounds.

The cost/benefit relationship so clearly indicated this bridge as a first priority that, as soon as economic stringency became relaxed, the Ministry of Transport authorised commencement of works and the bridge at Kincardine-on-Forth was completed in 1936.

With the opening of this bridge, the need for a crossing near Queensferry ceased to be of such pressing urgency. During the few years between its completion and the second world war, Kincardine Bridge, together with the ferry facilities coped more or less adequately with traffic needs.

But the demand for a bridge did not go away. In February 1937, the then Minister of Transport, Leslie Hore Belisha, attended a meeting in the Usher Hall, Edinburgh. Introducing him Lord Elgin reminded the audience that the minister had shown great courage in coming to Edinburgh after announcing in parliament that he was not convinced of the case for a bridge over the Forth.

Hore Belisha replied that instead of the political meeting he expected to attend, this event seemed to be a gathering of the Forth Bridge Protection Committee. He went on to remind them of the millions paid to Scotland from the Road Fund, including the £413,00 for the Kincardine Bridge and its approaches. The initial survey had been carried out, he said, but then became almost lyrical in the government's defence.

'We heard, and we had to pause in the tasks in which we were engaged to hear, the sound of tramping military feet in Europe; we heard the whirr of the lathe turning to make shells and we could almost sniff the nauseating poisonous gas.'

He didn't reject the notion of a bridge entirely, but said that the defence programme must have priority. Lord Elgin thought that the

The Mary Queen of Scots at North Queensferry Pier

Rail Bridge was lonely and needed a companion. The Lord Advocate suggested that if the minister came back to Edinburgh, he would still find that the noblest prospect to an Edinburgh citizen was a road bridge over the Forth.

In coronation year, enough money would probably have been spent on ceremonial to defray a great part of the three million estimated cost for the bridge. Hore Belisha told the government that he had considered proposals for three bridges, over the Forth, Severn and Humber rivers and come to the conclusion that there was no justification for them at the present moment.

This did not go down well with industry. With over four thousand steel workers unemployed, it was an ideal time for preparation work to begin. Hore Belisha visited the Mackintosh Rock site and when, in 1939, the Ministry of Transport finally agreed in principle with the need for a bridge, this site offered so many advantages to east coast traffic that it was the obvious choice. The start of the Second War, however, again ended any possibility of the bridge being built.

In addition to plans for a road bridge, other proposals put forward in the thirties and forties planned to make use of the existing rail bridge. In 1930 Messrs Mott, Hay & Anderson reported on the feasibility of embodying a second deck on the Forth railway bridge to take road traffic. The scheme did not find favour, principally because It would have been costly, and likely to be opposed by the railway company.

In 1948, another scheme was put forward by Sir Bruce White, of Wolfe Barry & Partners, which would provide an eighteen foot wide roadway and two thirty inch wide footways above the existing railway tracks. It was considered that the bridge was capable of bearing the additional load of the roadway, but in order to save weight, the viaducts carrying the railroad through the cantilevers were to be replaced by new construction of the same weight carrying both railway and roadway.

Small modifications were considered necessary on the existing suspended spans to allow the introduction of a road deck at a suitable height, whilst the approach spans were to be strengthened and raised.

These proposals were examined on behalf of the Ministry of Transport, by a panel which reported in 1954. It concluded that it was preferable to build a new and separate bridge. Meanwhile, other plans were afoot.

A tunnel scheme had been reported on by Mott, Hay and Anderson prior to the second world war. It would have been difficult to find the most suitable site, and it would probably have been necessary to construct a pilot tunnel before embarking on such a project as a traffic tunnel.

In 1954 a new and ingenious tunnel scheme to cross the river near the railway bridge was put forward by Mr G. A. Maunsell. His proposal was to provide an underwater bridge consisting of reinforced concrete tubes supported on piles to form a tunnel over the bed of the estuary but some seventy feet below mean sea level. These tubes were to be eighty four feet across, twenty six feet deep and up to seven hundred feet long, and were to be built in a graving dock, floated into position and lowered to the required depth.

The road bridge is still a dream

The underwater section would be 3800 feet long and would provide dual twenty two foot carriageways in separate compartments, and two ventilating ducts.

Again the Ministry of Transport set up a panel which concluded that the bridge proposals would be preferable, on the grounds that although first costs would be similar, maintenance and operation costs for the subway would be greater than for the bridge. Moreover, the approach roads to the tunnel would present considerable difficulties and would be less satisfactory than those which could be provided for the bridge.

When, after the war, an agreement was reached for a bridge using Mackintosh Rock, arrangements were made between the government and local authorities about how the money was to be raised and in 1947, The Forth Road Bridge Order was passed with the Forth Road Bridge Joint Board as the authority. It took more than ten years, however, for a start to be made.

By the fifties, it was clear that the ferry service could no longer cope with twentieth century volumes of traffic. The upsurge in car ownership, and road transport in general resulted in massive queues on both sides of the river, and the demand for an alternative crossing could no longer be ignored.

Discussions were held in London regarding proposals for the preliminary work necessary.

Before a start could be made on approach roads, some lands with houses in public and private ownership would have to be acquired. Problems arose later when not all the landowners were identified, and compulsory purchase orders were served, and the sale money put into a fund till owners could be traced.

Even before the decision to build the bridge had been published, Fife Council were approached regarding the re-housing of tenants in houses due for demolition when work began.

By 1957, the estimated cost of the bridge was fifteen million pounds and a full scale model was on show at the Ideal Homes Exhibition in Edinburgh. In February 1958, government approval was finally given for work to go ahead on the largest suspension bridge in Europe and the fourth largest in the world.

In the same year, the Forth Road Bridge Joint Board, comprised of representatives from the City of Edinburgh, the counties of Fife, West Lothian and Midlothian, the City and Royal Burgh of Dunfermline, and the Royal Burgh of Kirkcaldy, was set up and the following year Mott, Hay & Anderson were appointed Consulting Engineers.

The estimated cost of the road bridge and its approaches was £16.2 million, with some money to come from loans from central government and money and loans from the local authorities involved.

These were to be repaid by revenue from tolls and it was expected that payment would be completed within thirty years.

TAKING SHAPE

Shortly after the war, in addition to plans for a Forth Bridge, another scheme for a long span bridge over the River Severn was also being considered. Plans had been put forward in 1945 for a 3240 ft span bridge and an order under the Trunk Roads Act had been made for this project in 1947.

Since this bridge was of similar span to the planned Forth bridge, it was obviously desirable to consider the common problems together, and this was done, particularly in connection with aspects of the required research.

It was first thought that a bridge over the Severn was the prior need, and aerodynamic investigations were therefore instigated by the Ministry of Transport for the Severn Bridge in the knowledge that the data so obtained would be of equal use for the Forth.

A wind tunnel, unique in that it had a working chamber large enough to take a scale model of the whole bridge, and which could be slewed to allow wind effects to be studied across or along the bridge or at any intermediate angle, was built at Thurleigh, near Bedford in 1947. Extensive wind tests were carried out and the equipment used on these tests was transferred to the Forth for similar investigations into wind speed and direction.

During a test period of approximately eighteen months, several gusts of about a hundred miles an hour were recorded, so the new bridge was designed for a maximum wind speed of one hundred and ten miles an hour.

It was finally decided that the bridge over the Forth should take precedence, and much of the research and planning that went into the Forth Bridge, as well as specially designed equipment, was later used in the Severn Bridge.

The Forth Bridge was the first suspension bridge of any size built in the United Kingdom for nearly a hundred years and there were no engineers in the United Kingdom at that time, who had experience or knowledge of designing and constructing large suspension bridges. A start, therefore, had to be made from scratch.

As in every other research project, the first step was to survey the existing practice and knowledge. This had been acquired in the building, by engineers throughout the world, of about twenty major bridges with central spans varying from 1200 to 4200 feet.

The newly formed Forth team took nothing for granted, however, and began to search for better ways, if these were possible.

One of the main problems facing the bridge designers was the wind. The simple rules then existing for estimating the effects of ninety miles an hour winds on medium sized bridges were quite inapplicable to a structure where wind effects were a major factor.

The bridge would be similar in size to the one over the Tacoma Narrows, which connected the Olympic Peninsula with the mainland of Washington state, and which collapsed only four months after its opening in 1940. Aero-dynamics as a science was insufficiently understood at that time, but an investigation showed that the bridge did not absorb the turbulence of wind gusts. In addition, the narrow two lane roadway gave the centre span, 2800 feet long, a high degree of flexibility and with these two problems, the bridge basically shook itself apart.

Luckily the bridge was closed in time to prevent any loss of life, and the accident spurred on research into aero-dynamics and led to important advances in bridge design and building. Lessons were learned and

the engineers in charge of the Forth project were well aware of the problems facing them in constructing a bridge across a windswept tidal river.

Wind tests were carried out at the National Physical Laboratory and recording instruments were set up in 1947 at Severn and later at the Forth Bridge site. The measurements continued until 1954 on the Severn site and until 1957 on the Forth site. Wind conditions on the Severn were probably much more favourable than those on the Forth Bridge site.

Special anemometers recording speed, direction and inclination of the wind, were installed in 1951 after three years of development and trials. The recording charts, which eventually filled a room, were carefully studied and analysed.

In the 1950s, there were no calculators or computers as we know them today, but academics succeeded in producing workable computer programmes.

These provided information relevant for any span, if the length of both cable and span were known, and it was possible to determine the limitations which stress and distortion would place on any proposed erection sequence.

In fact, the span of the Forth Bridge superstructure was only sixty feet shorter than that originally designed for the Severn Bridge.

Sections of the tower arrive on the site next to the causeway

There were two other major breakthroughs. One was the design of the all-welded battle deck, which would carry the roadways, and which was designed and tested between 1946-49.

It was the first of its kind, and inspired by American practice and research, although Germans actually were the first to build modern battle deck bridges.

The design of the towers was the result of many years of thinking and arguing. Usually towers accounted for more than half the weight of the structural steel in a bridge and maximum efficiency in their design was therefore vital.

Approximate comparisons were made for steel and concrete towers and various methods of construction, and the final design resulted in a thirty per cent saving in the original estimated weight.

This design called for steel towers to be made up of a series of box like structures, prefabricated in a factory and carefully fitted together and erected on site.

During the process of bridge building various changes were made to the original designs because of improvements in the materials available, and using experience gained from other projects such as the Volta Bridge.

The Severn-Forth bridge project was analysed about ten times, each exercise taking months at a time, and every element was designed at least four times, and sometimes as many as twenty.

It was finally decided by the Government that the Forth Road Bridge should take precedence over the Severn Bridge, and in 1956 the Minister of Transport's functions in Scotland relating to roads, bridges and ferries were transferred to the Secretary of State for Scotland. Authority was given by the Government to proceed with the scheme in 1958.

With one exception all the main contracts were let by competitive tendering. The exception was that for the supply and erection of the superstructure of the suspension bridge.

For this a contract was negotiated with a consortium of three major bridge construction firms, Sir Wm. Arrol & Co. Ltd; the Cleveland Bridge and Engineering Co. Ltd; and Dorman Long (Bridge & Engineering) Co. Ltd.

At the time, there was no single engineering company equipped to carry out such a massive project, and there were fears that the contract might go abroad. The three companies became ACD and their combined expertise was more than equal to the challenge. And it was to prove quite a challenge.

It would be the first ever long span suspension bridge built in Britain, and the biggest to be built since Brunel's Clifton Bridge nearly a hundred years before.

This had been the longest in the world at the time, when Britain was leading the world in suspension bridge design.

Now America was in the forefront, with two of the biggest, The Golden Gate Bridge in San Francisco with a main span 4200 feet, and the George Washington Bridge in New York with one of 3500 feet. The Forth Bridge was to be smaller than these with a centre span of 3340 feet and side spans of 1340 feet.

structure grew. Much of the new bridge was fabricated elsewhere and erected on site.

Before construction could begin, however, the first stage involved building foundations for the piers and towers, and tunnelling deep into the earth to build the anchorages for the huge cables that would carry the bridge.

Work began in September 1958. An open pile structure was erected in the river and a causeway leading to it built out of more than ten thousand tons of rock and rubble, strong enough to take the heavy lorries of the steel contractors right up to the site of the pier.

The south pier was situated about 1250 feet from the south shore. The bed of the Forth had to be penetrated to a depth of one hundred feet and nearly two hundred tons of debris removed from the rock before work on the coffer dams could begin.

Three-quarters of a century separated the Forth rail and road bridges. The contrast between the riveted construction of the railway bridge and the clean lines of the towers of the road bridge is very marked. The 1890 bridge was built up of tens of thousands of pieces of steel, mostly too heavy to move without lifting tackle, and each part was straightened, bent, punched, drilled, bolted and unbolted, and riveted in place as the

Main tower fabrication trial assembly

The original form of the foundation for the south pier was rectangular, but after further borings on the site, a circular foundation in the form of a figure-of-eight steel frame was developed. It was towed across the river, and surrounded with sheet steel piling before being emptied of silt and gravel and pumped dry.

Two sixty foot caissons, the foundations for the south tower, were built and sunk without any mishap. Sir John Howard, whose firm had the contract for the bridge foundations, explained to the Dunfermline Chamber of Commerce how it was done.

Engineers thought it would be necessary to sink the foundations using compressed air as they had done with the rail bridge. Many lives had been lost using compressed air and it was thought to be worth trying to work in free air. Engineers impressed the need for caution. Materials had to be the best available and the workmanship perfect. They could not afford the possibility of another Tay Bridge disaster A new lubricating system was used to get through the very stiff boulder clay to the rock, the first time that such method of sinking monoliths had been adopted.

For the north pier, situated on Mackintosh Rock, thirty feet of rock had to be removed by under water blasting before a reasonably level base of clean rock could be achieved.

Eight divers worked continuously for over three months preparing the river bed. One of their main difficulties was the icy cold black water, which meant that they had difficulty in determining when all the hard boulder clay was removed from the whinstone rock. They used hoses from a fire pump to clean the river bed and the loose material was removed by an air lift.

Part of North Queensferry pier littered with bits and pieces ready for work to begin

The divers' attention to detail was revealed after the coffer dams were built and de-watering took place.

A large steel frame was floated on to the site, steel pilings placed round it, and made watertight with concrete before construction work could begin. The piers are one hundred and sixty eight feet long and fifty five feet wide, and rise thirty feet above the average river level. Designed by Giles Gilbert Scott, the piers have sloping sides and cutwater ends, and they are faced with granite chips.

Two anchorage tunnels, each twenty five feet in diameter, were built on the south shore, and two on the north measuring thirty two feet square.

Use was made of the natural rock configuration and tunnels were driven at an angle of thirty degrees. All were filled with concrete, eighty thousand cubic yards in all, and stiffened and supported by fifteen hundred tons of steel.

These were used to anchor the high tensile steel wires that make up the main suspension cables.

The original design of the main towers was considerably modified, as various stages of development were checked. The final dimensions were five hundred and twelve feet high and the towers made in eleven sections of prefabricated steel sections.

This was truly a national undertaking. Made by Arrols in Glasgow, the pieces were then shipped to Drem Airfield in East Lothian for protective treatment and for storage, before being transported to the bridge site. Other steelwork for the towers was fabricated at Middlesborough and Darlington.

One of the benefits of this approach was that different parts of the country gained from the project. In Midlothian, an area of unemployment, few skilled workmen were available for the grit blasting and zinc-spraying processes required.

The 85 foot diameter rings of steel are prepared ...

However, within a very short time, it was possible to train virtually unskilled labour so that a remarkably high standard was achieved.

Drem was seventy five miles from the north side of the Forth and the delivery of ten thousand tons of steel work for each end of the bridge to reach the right place at the right time must have been a formidable task.

Twenty five men erection crews worked on each tower. The north tower bases were delivered in June 1960 and the higher sections were erected by means of a climbing structure made of box girders.These provided accommodation for men and stores and all the equipment necessary for the tower's construction.

Special attention was given to safety factors, including anti-freezing devices, which were fitted on working platforms and hoists, to make them secure in adverse wind and weather conditions.

Severe weather in January and February 1961 caused the tower, which was then four hundred and seventy feet high, to oscillate in the wind, at one point moving several feet. Considerable delay was caused to the work because the jib of the derrick at the tower top had to be tied up and steel erectors were thrown about, bruised, suffered from sea sickness and had to be brought down to the ground.

A damping device was promptly devised. Two steel wire ropes were tied to the top of each leg of the tower and brought down to the ground and connected to a counterweight, with wire ties. This proved most effective.

These oscillations occurred only during erection when the towers were free standing, and as soon as the footbridge strands were erected, the towers were free from any such aerodynamic movement.

...and towed into position

During erection of the south tower a similar damping device was connected to the top of the ninth section, when the tower had reached a height of about four hundred feet. and it was subsequently raised and re-fixed to the legs of the tower immediately below the climbing structure in its highest position.

The top section, the upper cross girder of the tower was used as part of the climbing structure before being erected in its permanent position. It was completed in February 1961. The south tower was finished in June that year, and a small lift capable of taking three people was installed inside the leg of each tower.

The cable saddles, weighing thirty two tons each, were fixed to the top of the tower legs. The cables would eventually be two feet in diameter, seven thousand feet long and each be comprised of 11,618 wires, weighing three thousand seven hundred and twenty five tons.

The wire for these main cables, produced by Dorman Long (Steel) Ltd was delivered in one kilometre coils which were then wound on to large reels holding seven to eight tons.

The success of the bridge depended to a large extent on the high tensile steel wire cables. The production method for these was discovered by John A. Roebling in America more than a hundred years previously and been used by him on the construction of the Brooklyn Bridge in 1883.

The process had undergone continuous evolution in all the major suspension bridges built in the US since that time, but remained unaltered in principle.

Advice was sought from Roebling's American engineers and the cable was the only part of the superstructure to be built, more or less from scratch, on the site.

The cable spinning was controlled from the south side of the river, but before that could be done, catwalks had to be constructed.

Brian Smith, of Freeman, Fox and Partners, one of the two firms of consultant engineers, explained to the

The first wires are towed across the river by pontoon

Dunfermline Press that each pathway would be supported by eight wire ropes and would have three hand ropes on either side.

These would be lifted up between the tops of the five hundred foot high towers and extend downwards to ground level on each side of the river. The river would be closed to shipping for two to four hours a day for the two weeks that this work was going on. Ferry boats were not affected because they were downstream.

Two and a half miles of light steel wire mesh pathways, supported by parallel wire ropes were built, three feet below the level of the future cable. The twenty footbridge strands of one inch diameter, were manufactured by Bruntons (Musselburgh) Ltd, and brought to the site on huge reels. To erect the strands at site they were unreeled one at a time on to the bed of the river from north to south. In good weather, two strands were laid per tide, one upstream and one downstream.

The first operation was to haul the free end of the strand up and connect it to the top of the north side tower. The strand was then paid out across the river, lying on the bed except where it was laid across the stagings at each of the main piers, until the other end could be hauled to the top of the south side tower.

Meanwhile the barge returned to the north side to tow over the second strand, and about three hours after high water, by which time all shipping would have passed by, the strands were hoisted up into position by derricks on top of each of the main towers. The exact points along the length of the strand corresponding to the centre line of the towers had been marked previously so that the strand could be placed accurately in position and clamped in its temporary saddles at the tower tops.

When all strands had been erected they were carefully surveyed and any necessary adjustments made. These surveys were all made in the early morning before daylight.

Catwalks reach out to the main tower

22

Although work was considerably hampered by high winds and gales, all twenty strands and two winch haulage ropes were erected and adjusted within a month. The operation was controlled by radio telephone, and its timing agreed in advance with the Admiralty and the Forth Conservancy Board who gave their full co-operation. It was found possible to lift the strands in a fast-running tide and winds up to thirty miles an hour.

The footbridges were over nine feet wide, and floored by ten foot long panels of galvanised wire mesh with hardwood treads. They were supported along their length by galvanised wire strands, which ran parallel beneath them. In addition, two hand strands held the tops of parapets of lighter wire mesh, three and a half feet high on either side. Parapets giving such a degree of safety had never before been used on a catwalk, but in the bitter weather encountered on the Forth they proved their worth.

The structural parts of the footbridge were all steel; they were very light and strong, and offered as little obstruction as possible to the wind.

An electrical lighting system was installed throughout the length of the footbridges, but some items of electrical and other equipment first installed on the footbridges and elsewhere had to be modified to enable them to stand up to the arduous conditions of work and weather.

On one occasion, work was stopped all day by winds over forty five miles an hour followed by heavy snow in the evening. Next morning the slats on the footbridges were iced up and the wires frozen into the saddle grooves. The pulleys and control buttons on the winches were frozen and re-froze as fast as they were freed.

Fixing the side panels to the hand rails

Lamp heaters had to be fitted to the control units of all unreeling machines, and heaters were incorporated in to motors, and provision made for an external air-warmer on each machine.

Seven tubular-framed cross bridges, fixed between the catwalks, provided access between them and also reduced wind movement. Special bracing helped prevent the catwalks swaying in the wind, and enabled them to withstand gusts of up to one hundred and twenty miles an hour.

Once the catwalks were complete, cable spinning could begin. In spinning, loops of wire are carried over the span on a grooved spinning wheel which is attached to a tramway drive or aerial rope way. When the loops reach the far anchorage they are pulled off the spinning wheel by hand and placed round a strand shoe which connects them to the anchorage.

At the near end the loops of wire are also placed round a strand shoe of the near anchorage. Other loops are then carried across on the wheel and so the spinning proceeds. Each wire is adjusted for level at the centre of the main span and in the side spans, initially against a guide wire, to ensure that all wires have the same sag. The cables are each made up of thirty seven strands, with an average number of three hundred and fourteen wires per strand. All the wires in one strand are connected to the same shoe, thirty seven strand shoes being provided at each anchorage.

Two overhead tramways, one for each catwalk, consisted of an endless rope, one inch in diameter and nearly three miles long, which was made up of two steel wire ropes. Driven by electric hydraulic machines, these tramways carried two spinning wheels, on one each tram, travelling in opposite directions, shuttling to and fro across the river each trip laying ten miles of wire.

In all, they would make about fifteen hundred journeys across the river to complete the cable.

Spinning wires above the saddles

Wire handlers were stationed at four hundred foot intervals, lights and telephone lines were installed along the length of the catwalk and electric control signals were used for adjusting the wires.

Because the builders were trying to achieve something that had not been tackled before, new skills and equipment for cable spinning had to be acquired.

Handling wires over the saddles

The enormous cost of this equipment, which had to be specially purchased, was justified by the fact that it could be used again, with very little alteration, on the Severn Bridge.

The spinning was done throughout most of the winter of 1961-62, and finished in August 1962. Throughout that time, it was seldom possible to reach the desired capacity of the equipment for long periods, partly because it was new to all personnel but mostly because of the wind. One engineer claimed that it was a miracle that the job had been accomplished, because no-one had ever been faced with the problem of spinning wire in such conditions.

The men who worked on these high wires, five hundred feet above the Forth, were called spider men and many moved from country to country wherever bridge building was going on. They were a cross between trapeze artists and ballerinas, moving with grace, agility and confidence, and had nerves of steel.

For a press reporter, taken to the top of the south tower in a lift, which took two and a half minutes, the view was stupendous.

He did not enjoy returning via the catwalks. Stepping gingerly from slat to slat, he was egged on by workmen telling him it was quite safe and advising him to take it at a run.

One thing the spider men were all agreed on, that the Forth was the worst bridge they had ever worked on, and for one reason only. The weather. They were hampered by fog, frost, sleet, snow and worst of all high winds.

Harold Mills of the Roebling company was amazed that work went on in weather that would never have been considered possible in America. He had never seen spinning start so late in the year, and was full of admiration for British innovations, which were improvements on the American methods and used for the first time on any bridge.

The wire was thicker than that used in America and conditions were so bad that in ten minutes, winds could rise from fifteen to forty miles an hour, and spinning was impossible. The work was new to the men; they were trained on the catwalks and in the sheds.

The engineers not only had to train their workers but had to be out at night, surveying levels of the wires spun during the day. They sometimes worked from seven in the evening till four in the morning, on top of their ordinary day's work.

All the cable spinning was done by men working on two eight-hour shifts, daytime from eight till four, and evening four till midnight. In order to permit uninterrupted spinning there were no stops for tea or meal breaks.

Tea and hot soup were delivered periodically by means of an urn strapped on the back of a tea boy and meals were eaten between the passing of the wheels. In spite of their exposed position, high over the Forth on bitter, cold nights, little if any shelter could be provided for the cable spinners on account of the necessity for keeping obstructions to wind down to a minimum. In order to get good production, fifty or sixty men, stationed in groups along six thousand feet of exposed footbridge, had to work in concert by day or night, in good weather and bad, unless work had to be stopped because of rain or high winds.

The Forth Road Bridge is situated in latitude 56° north, much further north than any major suspension bridge in the world, and in an area notorious for its high winds and storms. Cable spinning is particularly susceptible to interruption by bad weather and although attempts were made early on is particularly susceptible

Strand adjusting equipment on the south tower

to interruption by bad weather and although attempts were made early on to spin in winds exceeding forty miles an hour, experience showed that adjustment of the wires was not really practicable in winds over thirty, even though the men were willing to carry on working.

The time lost by bad weather, amounting to a third of the total period, compares with a maximum loss of about five per cent of spinning time suffered in any of the long-span suspension bridges in the U.S.A.

The worst delay occurred early in 1962, when only four or five strands had been spun in each cable and the work was perhaps at its most vulnerable stage. On the night of Sunday, 11 February a severe storm lasting some twenty hours with wind speeds of eighty to one hundred miles an hour struck the site.

The main cable strands on the north west side span broke loose from the ropes lashing them to the catwalk and thrashed about, hammering against the sides of the footbridge hour after hour, smashing the electrical installations and tangling the wires.

To a less serious extent the same thing happened in the north east side span, and the north half of the east main span, although there the cable did not break loose from the walk.

Live wire sheaves, telephones, lighting, signal panels and electric cables were wrecked, hand posts bent, and about a thousand feet of the parapet mesh torn away. Two telephones were destroyed and several live wire sheaves disintegrated and were buried amongst the cable wires.

Gale force winds persisted for the next three days, during which the opportunity was taken to remake lashings that had broken loose and to tie everything securely. On Friday, a second storm, even worse than the first and of similar duration, struck the bridge, but nothing broke loose and no significant damage was sustained

During both storms, which blew from the south west, veering to the north west, lateral deflection of the catwalks in the main span was seen to be between fifty five and sixty feet at the height of the gale.

During the following week, which was mostly fine and calm, all hands, including erectors, electricians, fitters and carpenters, were concentrated on repairing the damage. By midweek all repairs except the disentangling of individual cable wires and resorting into strands had been completed.

Sections of catwalk ready to be constructed

The combing of the wires, however, proved a formidable task. They were crossed and re-crossed, and incredibly mixed for hundreds of feet, both in the main and side spans and it took till the end of March to repair the damage. Fortunately, no part of the permanent structure suffered any damage.

As the cables were spun, the suspender wires, each made up of two bights of steel wire ropes which would support the roadway, were looped over special steel grooves formed for the purpose at the top of the cable bands. The sockets at the lower ends were ready to receive the steel of the suspended structure. The height of the suspenders varied from nine foot six at the lowest point, to over three hundred feet near the towers. They weighed up to four tons, had to be delivered by two work cars and handled several hundred feet in the air, often in stormy conditions, so the greatest care was needed.

The twin ropes of each suspender were unreeled at the tower top platforms and slid out along the cat walks, supported by two work cars. When the appropriate cable band was reached, the socketed ends were lowered one on each side of the main cable until the bights of the ropes landed in their cable band grooves.

It was not possible to adjust them, so it was therefore essential that they should all be made to exactly the right length. White lines were painted down the side of each rope so that any twist in it which could appreciably affect its length could be detected and removed.

Spacers had to be fitted about a hundred and fifty feet from the top of the six longest suspenders in order to prevent the ropes from clashing together in storms of wind.

The suspender ropes were then given four coats of paint, using equipment used on air-operated cradles. They were then ready for the next stage, when the bridge would finally start to take shape.

The suspender wires are in place ready to take the next section of the decking

*Left – shoring up the roof
of the anchorage tunnel*

*Right – the anchorage chambers
for the cables that carry the bridge*

Walkways stretch across the river

One of the giant wheels that carried the cable wires

Right – After the cables were compacted blocks and covers had to be fitted to the saddle casting

CLOSING THE GAP

The steelwork of the suspended structure was erected in two stages, and work was begun with crane girders working outwards from either side of the main towers. The steel work was delivered by road along the causeways and jetties to the staging at the base of each tower.

It was then lifted by another derrick and landed on a temporary loading bay at deck level, from which it was run out by self-propelled bogies on rail tracks to each erection front.

So that there would be no delay when the cables had been completed and the first suspenders erected, the first ninety foot lengths of deck were cantilevered out from each side of each tower and the derricks assembled on them before the end of cable spinning.

When each panel of steelwork had been assembled and connected to the suspenders, the temporary crane tracks were extended, and the derrick moved out to the end of the panel in order to erect the next one.

The work continued in this way until eighteen panels had been erected on either side of each tower. Then work on the two fronts in the main span had to be halted until the remaining four panels had been built in each side span and connected to their bearings at the side towers.

During deck erection, not less than twenty steel erectors worked on each of the four fronts, with an additional back shift of about sixty men employed from four in the afternoon until midnight during the summer months to take advantage of the long light evenings. As long as daylight lasted they worked aloft, but at about 9.30 p.m. they came down to the stagings at the foot of the towers. Here it was fenced and they could work in safety by electric light assembling material ready for erection next day. It would have been unsafe to continue steelwork erection at such a height after dusk, even by artificial light, because of the shadows that are cast.

Safety was of paramount importance. The Contractors decided at an early stage to use four safety net assemblies, one under each of the working fronts, during erection of the suspended structure.

Each assembly weighed some fifteen tons, fully covered the length and width of three panels, and measured nearly two hundred feet long and a hundred and fifty feet wide.

At that time, no British Standard specification on safety nets existed, because they were not in general use in British engineering though they had been used in the United States, and so little information was obtainable. A comprehensive series of tests was undertaken by Associated Bridge Builders Ltd, at Drem to investigate the whole problem.

These included the material to be used for making the nets, and especially its strength, elasticity, durability, and lightness and the method of construction.

Left – compacting cables

Right – spinning

Sample nets were tested by dropping a weight of about two hundred and fifty pounds, shaped like a man's body, onto them at the middle, near the sides, and near the corners, from heights up to thirty feet. The best results were finally obtained with nets of hand made nylon or Terylene cord of not less than one thousand pounds breaking strain.

These were much lighter and more elastic than equivalent manila ropes.

Designs were made for the supporting framework, and a means of moving the assembly out to extend beyond the erection front as erection proceeded, had been devised. The supporting framework of each assembly consisted of tubular steel work and could be moved by hand winches.

Throughout construction, safety measures for the workmen were considered to be of prime importance. These included the compulsory wearing of helmets, which saved a number of lives, by everyone on the steel work, and the provision of sets of safety harness, which were a marked improvement on safety belts, for any men requiring them.

The three senior engineers and the three senior foremen were appointed safety supervisors. Regular meetings were held at which safety matters were discussed and the attention of engineers and foremen was constantly directed to all safety aspects of the work. This ranged from keeping the site tidy and access gangways clear, to the provision of adequate guards on machines, and avoidance of any dangerous practices.

No safety officer, as such, was employed, be cause the job was too complex for this. It was judged better to charge all engineers and foremen with the responsibility for safety in their sectors.

Decisions to provide safety appliances which cost thousands of pounds have to be made at a high level, and designs for them prepared many months before they are needed on the site.

In spite of all the precautions taken, however, there were three fatal accidents on the erection of the superstructure. Two of these accidents were caused by the failure of a safety net, which had been put there solely in order to provide the final element of safety.

Experience had shown that men work more quickly and freely on structural steel work if safety nets are provided beneath them. The nets, which were used throughout the length of the main and side spans, saved at least two lives. Unfortunately, in a tragic accident during the last months of the work, one complete assembly broke away from the bridge and fell into the river.

This accident took place in June 1964, a few months before the bridge opening ceremony. A squad of steel erectors was moving a safety net in the middle of the centre span when it collapsed, and three men plunged a hundred and seventy feet into the Forth. Two were killed, and one of the bodies was never recovered. A third man, John Geddes from Edinburgh was rescued, clinging almost unconscious to a piece of wood, and a fourth man, John Smith, from Glasgow, was injured on the bridge, but did not fall into the water.

Although it fell a hundred and seventy five feet and sank in two hundred feet of water, most of the structure was dragged up by the Admiralty and recovered.

Erecting diagonal trusses in side span with safety nets underneath

It appeared that the disaster must have been caused by some structural failure, but the steelwork was so damaged by its fall and recovery that no evidence of the nature of the failure could be found.

The other fatal accident happened through a one-in-a-million chance when a painting gantry weighing four and a half tons was being lowered by two hand winches from the top of the south tower. One of the winches failed and a piece of metal flying from the disintegrating gearing struck a man thirty feet away. He was hit on the head just below his safety helmet, and was killed.

The painting gantry, falling from a height of four hundred and fifty feet, brought down the bracket crane which in turn damaged the storm system under the side span. Although the catwalk was badly shaken, no men were thrown off. The gangway finally landed on the south staging, causing damage to the structure and the material stacked on it.

Altogether, the bridge cost seven lives, compared with fifty seven for the rail bridge. Four were killed during the building of the main structure and three during the construction of the northern approaches.

A bronze memorial plaque commemorating the men killed was unveiled in the bridge car park by Sir Duncan Weatherstone, Edinburgh's Lord Provost, in 1965.

There were miraculous escapes, as is bound to be the case in such a dangerous and enormous undertaking, and there were many near-misses and accidents. One of the first casualties was Forester Smilie, who was tunnelling seventy feet underground at the north anchorage when tons of concrete caved in on him. He felt he was lucky to get out alive and was proud to have been involved in what he called 'a challenge, something for Scotland's progress.'

Andrew Blunt, a spider man, fell thirty five feet and was saved by a safety net. According to newspaper reports, this made him a member of the exclusive 'Halfway to Hell' Club, open only to men who fell while building bridges, and lived to tell the tale.

In 1963, Danny Slattery fell a hundred and eighty feet from the deck of the bridge, higher than the world high diving record at that time. No-one expected him to survive, imagining that every bone in his body would be broken, but he escaped injury except for breaking a small bone in his leg.

Edward Peadon, a crane driver from Inverkeithing, was lucky. He was one of the operators that drove the wheel over when they were spinning. He recalled something going wrong with the hydraulics and the wheel running back into the anchorage, but he escaped injury.

William Nelson, from Loanhead, a painter, was working on the top of the south tower when the scaffolding fell some forty feet, putting him in hospital for a week.

Despite wearing his safety helmet, Rapponnie Gilmour, a research engineer from Hampshire, received severe head injuries from a spanner which fell three hundred feet from the south tower on to his head when erectors were dismantling a crane.

The workmen look like midgets against these trusses

Erecting a foot way panel with the main span gantry

In August 1962, three men and a girl were injured when boulders came hurtling through the roofs of houses in Rosyth during blasting operations at the site of the approach road workings.

The McElvie family, had a lucky escape. It look two men to lift the boulder which came through the roof of their bedroom. Luckily the family were not at home at the time.

Ann Nellies, a nurse at the Dunfermline and West Fife Hospital remembered men coming in with minor injuries, but overall the safety record on the bridge was excellent.

In common with all sections of the bridge, the final decking was the result of several design changes. Some months before the start of deck erection, the contractors had a series of tests carried out under the direction of the National Physical Laboratory at Teddington, to determine the aerodynamic stability of the suspended steel work in the main span during erection.

These tests were all made on a model in the wind tunnel and the results showed which items of steel work could safely be erected in the first stage of its construction, because temporary distortions could occur before the two halves of the deck were lined up at mid-span.

As a result, engineers were able to determine the safest way to ensure that the deck would remain stable in winds up to a hundred miles an hour, the maximum wind speed employed in the tests.

As early as 1949, the Road Research Laboratory was consulted, and tests were again carried out, this time to discover the most reliable material for providing a durable, impervious and non-skid surface. Tests were still going on in 1964 when the bridge was nearing completion.

Two types of material were used in the roadway construction. In the main span the decks are of steel plates on which a layer of asphalt, one and a half inches thick, has been laid. In the side spans there is also asphalt surfacing but, there, this was laid on reinforced concrete slabbing.

This important difference in construction was planned to minimise imbalance of loading on the main towers. The weight of the main span is naturally greater than the weight of the two smaller spans.

The footway and cycle deck panels were thinly coated with rubberised bitumen and spread with fine granite chips.

In the first stage of deck construction, the stiffening trusses, cross girders, lateral bracing, most of the cantilever brackets, and four of the six eight feet wide pieces of battle deck in each panel, were put in place. Stiffening trusses are in effect large open boxes, with diagonal bracing on all four sides and cross girders spanning across each box to support the road deck itself.

The function of the truss is to stiffen the cable and distribute the loads more evenly along its length. They are necessary because the main cables carrying the deck are substantial, but owing to their great span, are very flexible and would easily deflect if heavy loads were hung directly from them.

All the steelwork for trusses and roadways, about fifteen thousand tons in all, was brought to the site as required and taken out to the main piers along the causeways. Cranes on the tower legs lifted each section on to bogies at deck level so that they could be run out ready for erection.

The steel was erected piece by piece to make up a sixty foot panel between suspenders As each panel was completed it was attached to the suspenders and the crane moved forward on to it ready to commence work on the next panel. In the second stage, which was not begun until shortly before the steelwork had been joined at mid-span, the erection of the remaining

panels of battle deck, the footway and cycle deck panels, crash barriers, and parapets was completed.

Trials were also carried out on the alignment of battle deck panels and the first of many movable welding platforms or stagings were assembled below the main span deck and the first panels prepared for welding.

However, there were problems with welding because of the protective zinc coating on the panels, and welders working below the deck on hand welding of troughs complained of the fumes arising from the zinc. This necessitated provision of anti-fume masks, extractors and blowing in air when conditions were bad.

For the welding of the main span in the first pass four movable stagings were provided below the deck.

When the second stage was complete, the steelwork was joined at mid-span, and this was done at a ceremony attended by the chairman of the Forth Road Bridge Joint Board on December 20, 1963. Cranes on both sides of the gap were moved forward and two sixty foot long box girders, decorated with a

The carriageways begin to take shape

Union Jack and the Lion Rampant, were swung into position.

The two parts of the suspended steelwork met at the middle, with a gap of only a few inches. Hydraulic jacking gear was then used to release the temporary pins holding the ends of the deck and the two halves of the deck met at mid span.

A section of the road deck with safety nets underneath

In order to start erection of all the remaining deck, two erection gantries, intended to work out from the towers towards mid-span, were designed at site. Assembled on the second panel out from each tower, these gantries completed the erection of the roadway battle decks, the cantilevered footway/cycle tracks, and the crash barriers, panel by panel as they moved towards mid-span.

Designed narrow enough to pass inside the suspenders, they travelled on temporary rail tracks and had hinged cantilevers at the ends which could be raised for the erection of the panels of footways and cycle decks. After completing their work in the main span they were used to assemble crash barriers and grillages in the side spans.

Once all the roadwork had been done, telephone and lighting installed, the erection cranes and catwalks were dismantled and the bridge was ready for the mass of traffic that awaited it.

It was a great achievement. According to the engineers report:

'Over a period of almost exactly twenty years, many people were involved in the evolution of this great project, from the man who for seven years attended the wind recording instruments in all weathers and at all times of night and day, to the leaders of the team, Sir David Anderson, Sir Ralph Freeman and Sir Gilbert Roberts.

Some had passed away and others had taken to other fields, but a few lucky ones were able to share in the final accomplishments. The achievement, however, would not have been possible without the leadership of the few and the devoted toil of the many.'

Left – view from under the superstructure   *Right – the south span seen from the centre span*

Left – May 1963
The piers holding the side spans
of the bridge
are in position

Right – View of the site
from the north side
with the viaduct piers
in the foreground

*Left – The road deck reaches
out, dwarfing the houses
underneath*

*Right – The north side
steel work is complete
and panels of deck
reach out from both sides
of the main towers*

*Left – The concrete base
for the carriageway
is finished and work
has begun on railing
the foot/cycle path*

*Right – The north side
viaduct is complete with
centre spans ready
for surfacing*

An uphill walk to the tower

The saddles on the main side towers

The main and side towers are complete and ready for the catwalks and cable wires

The road deck grows out from the central towers

Part of the cable spinning mechanism

The cable wires are fixed through the saddles on the side tower

The roadway is laid in sections

An almost complete main tower

A view of the decking from beneath the viaduct pillars.......and a pipe eye view of the towers and catwalks

One of the topping out ceremonies

A quiet moment on top of the bridge

Maintenance walkway under the carriageway

The lattice work under middle section of road

A view from the safety boat of the two centre sections of the decking

The last box girders sections of the bridge are in place

North tower with defences

North east cable cradle

Views from North and South Queensferry

A GREAT PROSPECT

At a meeting in Edinburgh in 1937, the then Minister of Transport, Hore Belisha was told by Scotland's Lord Advocate that the noblest prospect to an Edinburgh citizen would be a road bridge across the Forth.

Imagine then, the feelings of those seeing for the first time, this culmination of the grand plan, this wide sweep of dual carriageway leading to what must have appeared a delicate, fragile structure.

The great prospect

The bridge was just a part, albeit the most important one, of the whole Forth Road Bridge project. Old roads had to be upgraded and new approach roads built, including dual carriageway of four and a half miles on the southern side and three and a half miles on the northern side. Minor access roads extend for eight miles and there were twenty four minor bridges.

On the north side, new approach roads extended to Dunfermline with diversions at Welldean, Castlandhill and Masterton Road, and included the widening and extending of Admiralty Road to Hillend.

Altogether, there were seven principal junctions involving five miles of connecting and slip roads; twenty four foot carriageways were provided with cycle tracks and foot paths.

The collapse of the Masterton Flyover

The base for the south approach roads was the waste shale bings at Dalmeny. To ensure its suitability, an experimental embankment was built in three sections, and the most successful mixture was used.

The St Margaret's Head cutting was originally planned as a tunnel but the rock formation proved to be too difficult. The rock was split by blasting, a difficult and dangerous task because the railway was only six hundred feet away, and the nearest buildings about half that distance. Half a million cubic yards of rock were removed and used as filling at Welldean.

Bridges were basically reinforced concrete slab-type spans, except over railway tracks, where steelwork or pre-cast concrete was used.

The six hundred feet long Masterton Viaduct is the largest single structure on the approach roads. It was also the scene of one of the worst accidents of the whole Forth Bridge project. While still under

The search for survivors

construction, it collapsed on Friday, June 22nd 1962, at half past nine in the morning. A gang of four workmen dismantling scaffolding underneath the bridge was trapped beneath hundreds of tons of concrete rubble and twisted steel.

Two men, Cornelius Sweeney and Charles Gormley, died instantaneously. Their bodies were not recovered till the next day Michael Cusick and Thomas Bennett were rescued after two and a half hours later and taken to the Dunfermline and West Fife Hospital but Bennett died a few days later. An eye witness said that if the accident had happened five minutes later, the men would have stopped for their tea break.

'I just heard a crack,' he said and the whole thing eased forward. A joiner working on top jumped clear….we could hear the trapped men yelling for help.'

Welders with acetylene burners cut through the debris of steel and a team of men from the Coal Board's Mines Rescue Station at Cowdenbeath played a major part in releasing the survivors.

One of those who escaped was James Docherty from Kelty.

'I was working at the south east corner,' he told the Dunfermline Press, 'when I heard a rumbling noise like the sound of thunder, and when I came down the ladder the bridge was gone.'

The 1823 Cramond Brig

At an inquiry into the accident later that year, experts disagreed over the cause of the collapse. The foundations had been dug forty feet deep and there was no evidence of mine workings or subsidence in the area. Ground movement was blamed.

The final section of the approach roads on the south side of the river, which extended to Barnton, on the outskirts of Edinburgh, necessitated the building of a new bridge over the River Cramond, close to the Cramond Brig Hotel.

Sunday afternoon sightseers

The original bridge over the river, designed by Rennie and built in 1823, had eight semi-circular masonry arches. Consideration was given to retaining its form and appearance but this was not practicable. A single lane bridge was built alongside the original one, and traffic was diverted to this while the bridge was being demolished. This took two months and involved drilling seventeen hundred holes for five hundred pounds of gelignite.

Traffic was stopped for only thirty minutes during blasting. Later, when the second lane was built, the whole bridge was closed to traffic for a weekend, and restricted to single lane working for the following week. Altogether, the Cramond Bridge took twenty two months to build.

Originally, under surface heating was installed in the area on both sides of the toll booths but this was later removed.

The administration building provided offices for the Bridgemaster and his staff and accommodation for inspectors, toll collectors, clerical and outdoor maintenance staff.

At the rear was a garage and yard for bridge maintenance vehicles. When the bridge opened, the staff of seventy six consisted of the Bridgemaster and his deputy, clerical staff, inspectors, patrol and maintenance men., and toll collectors.

During the whole history of the bridge planning and construction, the subject that caused most dissension was that of tolls. Much of the early argument revolved around the legality of the imposition of charges. The agreement made with the government in 1947, and again in 1957 which had enabled the building of the bridge to go ahead, had been made on the basis of tolls being levied.

The government's view was that where large bridge or tunnel projects brought particular and identifiable benefits, such as the avoidance of a long detour, the tolls should be charged.

The economic situation, however, had changed radically by 1963 and it was felt that tolls constituted an additional tax burden. Government policy was inconsistent, with some schemes being treated more favourably than others.

The call for abolition was supported by practically every local authority, from The Scottish Council of Development and Industry, The STUC, the Scottish Tourist Board, the Scottish branch of the Federation of British Industries and the National farmers Union of Scotland.

The point was made that if ever there was a time to foster trade and development in Scotland, this was it, but there was evidence of developers hesitating to introduce new industries.

By 1963, though the campaign to abolish tolls had to accept defeat, there was still uncertainty about the level of charges. Industrial and private housing developers were trailing their feet, the possibility of high tolls said to be retarding the development of what were seen as major growth points in Fife.

The coming of the bridge had already encouraged the 'Fife Facelift', the transformation of run down areas, the removal of unsightly coal bings and their replacement with green fields.

Tolls were finally fixed at two shillings and sixpence for private cars and there was no shortage of motorists happy to hand over their half crown pieces. By the end of the first week, peak hour traffic was up to twelve hundred cars an hour, and the average takings eight hundred pounds a day.

Forty years on, the argument about tolls still rumbles on. The charges remain even though the bridge was paid for by the mid 1980s.

One of the early toll payers

The decking for the carriageways begins to grow...

...and is connected to the suspender wires

The decking reaches out from both sides of the main towers

Ready for opening day

OPENING DAY

For the people who had watched the bridge, this addition to the great wonders of the world, grow in stature and splendour, the opening day was looked forward to with tremendous excitement.

The opening day would be a new beginning, a culmination of the social and economic dreams of over forty years. From the time when the first serious proposals were put forward in 1923, local authorities, on both sides of the water, looked forward to a period of increasing prosperity. The bridge's inauguration would be a historic occasion, the day that Fife gave up its position as almost an island and became linked to the rest of Scotland with this magnificent new addition to the national road system.

Great things were planned. The Queen would officially declare the bridge open. Sixteen thousand people had been invited to watch the ceremony from reserved accommodation in specially constructed stands, and many more thousands were expected to gather in the immediate vicinity of the bridge. Everyone was sure it would be a day to remember.

There was, however, a problem that no-one had allowed for and that man's ingenuity could not deal with. The early morning mist, which is so much a feature of a September morning on the Forth, was making itself felt. Wilfred Taylor, writing in The Scotsman the next day described what happened in a piece entitled The Slow Unveiling.

In the Royal compound at this end of the bridge we explained to a Londoner the phenomenology of the haar which was as dense as a thicket at ten o'clock. Here, in the Lothians, we are mostly puritans by heredity. Any access, or excess of pleasure makes us feel uncomfortable so we take out a policy that protects us against too much of a good thing. At the beginning of the week we had some wonderful days of blue and green and gold. The scene was ablaze with local colour. The sun shone from cloudless skies and we knew that at this rate our immortal souls would be in jeopardy. To restore this balance we realised that arrangements would have to be made to drain all the light and the colours away so that we wouldn't cast clear-cut shadows in the morning sun.

Arrangements, it seemed, had been made to cast a blight on the occasion. From early in the morning, excited spectators gathered for the opening of a bridge they couldn't even see. Everyone knew that the weather would be marvellous later in the day. The question was how much later?

From his vantage point on the roof of the administration building, Taylor described the roadways beyond the toll gates melting away into nothingness. Near him, Tom Fleming was speaking softly into a BBC microphone, while a television camera was trained on a blown up picture of the bridge. Richard Dimbleby was on the job somewhere, but unseen. As the clock ticked slowly towards eleven o'clock, the sun began to struggle through, but

68

visibility was so bad that the fly past had to be cancelled.

Slowly the mist was being rolled back, Taylor wrote *We could count five, then seven arches in the viaduct. On the roof the sun was quite warm and our shadow had come back. The fly-past was off but we could hear a whirly-bird loudly stuttering somewhere. The royal party arrived to a rather thin cheer. A man with a telescope told us that the Queen was looking lovely...*

As Her Majesty delivered her speech the bridge was very slowly being unveiled, We could see all the arches in the viaduct and tie south tower was almost imperceptibly giving the lie to the sceptics who said that it wasn't there. The first cantilever span on the railway bridge was ever so gently sweeping the mist off its shoulders. A white launch floated on nothing. The guns thundered from the invisible ships.

Someone informed us that they had been loaded with mist-dissolving charges. Someone else added that the Queen would be returning by the ferry after all. We could see the flags on the top of the now solid-looking tower. Rockets puffed up into the clear sky high above the railway bridge.

As the Royal cavalcade slowly rolled out over the bridge, bands played the National Anthem and the ships in the river could be seen through the haze. Taylor and other reporters watched the rest of the proceedings on television.

By the time the Queen stepped aboard one of the ferry boats for the trip back to South Queensferry, the promise of a beautiful day had been fulfilled. The Forth's day of the century had looked like being an anti-climax, but instead of lamenting the fog, editors made a feature of it.

The Queen inspects the commemorative plaque...

The Courier's account claimed that Mother Nature stepped in and provided something the planners had never envisaged – an unveiling ceremony. Ninety minutes before the Queen was due to arrive, visibility was down to thirty yards, and both Forth Bridges were invisible. From dawn, throngs of people – from eighty to a hundred thousand according to various estimates – had made their way to the bridge. The brightly coloured coats and hats of the women made splashes of colour that vied with the two thousand flowers that decked the royal dais. The Rev. A.D. Stirling of South Queensferry, in his prayer of dedication, remembered the men who had been killed during the bridge's construction, and the Lord Provost of Edinburgh spoke of them when he invited the Queen to open the bridge.

'We cannot forget that lives were lost during this amazing engineering exercise... but today there must be a tribute all the great minds and the great hands which fashioned it.'

In her speech, the Queen recalled how the first plans for the bridge had been drawn up over forty years before.

'Today, after six years of work, this immense engineering project is finished and ready for use. All Scotland has been following the progress of the work with great interest, and I know that everyone would like me to congratulate the designers, contractors and workmen on their triumph of engineering skill...

I need hardly emphasise the economic and commercial value of this link between the Lothians and the Kingdom of Fife. The flow of commercial traffic which it will make possible is bound to have a

...and greets special guests

most stimulating effect throughout this part of Scotland, and I am certain it will bring great benefits to the economy of the whole of Scotland...

The ceremony in which we are engaged bridges the centuries as well as the Forth. There has probably been a sea passage near this point since the dawn of history, but the ferry owes its name to my ancestor, Queen Margaret, wife of Malcolm Canmore, who crossed the Forth many times on her journeys between Edinburgh and Dunfermline... May this bridge bring prosperity and convenience to a great many people in the years ahead.'

At the end of the Queen's speech, a twenty one gun salute was fired by the Royal Navy ships lying unseen under the bridge. Hooters blared and flags flew from the bridge towers. Rockets were fired from the Rail Bridge. After inspecting the marble obelisk recording the names of those responsible for the bridge design and construction, the Royal party went through the tollgates and so on over the bridge. Another shorter ceremony took place at the north end before they returned to North Queensferry for the trip back on the ferry boat, *Queen Margaret.*

After taking part, two of the twenty five ships involved in the ceremony collided under the bridge. *HMS Lion*, flagship of the home fleet, was still at anchor when she was hit by frigate *Lowestoft*, which was getting under way. It sustained damage to the bow and forward structure, but *Lion* was only slightly damaged. Both ships were taken in the Royal Naval Dockyard for inspection and repair. A second incident was described by a Courier reporter. He had travelled from Dundee aboard the *HMS Montrose*, which was supposed to be the first ship in the line when the Queen opened the bridge.

At 10.45, the *Montrose* bumped into the Beamer Rock. The crew did not see the opening but they heard a distant fanfare and the twenty one gun salute. *'Someone said That's it opened then. We were all very disappointed.'*

It was a gala day for Scotland's newspapers. Hundreds of column inches were taken up with photographs of the great occasion, and lists of the great and the good who were presented to Her Majesty: provosts, sheriffs, judges, heads of the engineering firms and representatives of the men who worked for six years to finish the bridge, members of parliament and officers of the police and armed forces.

All the newspapers were in agreement about the magnificence of the new structure, including one which shall remain nameless but which claimed it as *'a monument in Scotland to the engineering skill of the north of England, and in particular to the bridge builders of Durham and North Yorkshire, who have helped to span the world.'*

Many more column inches, however, were devoted to the scenes later in the day. Headlines ranged from *Thrill of A Lifetime* to *My Nightmare Journey*. Robert Morrison from Broughty Ferry had arrived early at the north end of the bridge and was surprised to find himself first in the queue to cross, but by the time the bridge opened for traffic around five thirty, he was at the head of a two mile double line of traffic. There were twenty five miles of queues as traffic converged along all four approach routes, the longest stretching to Barnton, on the outskirts of Edinburgh. An AA spokesman said that nothing like this had ever taken place in the history of motoring in Scotland, with an estimated fifteen to eighteen thousand cars waiting to cross. Five hundred cars crossed in the first fifteen minutes and by eight o'clock, a peak of five thousand cars an hour had been reached.

The Bridgemaster Robert Wilson had not seen the like, even in America. *The Scotsman* welcomed the speeding up of communications between Lothians and Fife which would bring new life to the centre of Scotland. On that first evening, however, the description by the *Scottish Daily Express* was more apt. From fifteen hundred feet up in the sky, it said that everything on wheels seemed to be crawling towards the bridge, like a steel caterpillar. People were getting out of cars to walk on the grass verge or to have tea from their flasks. Cars tried in vain to do U-turns.

One reporter claimed that it had taken him eight hours to do a seventy mile trip. The approach roads from Kirkcaldy, Dunfermline and Rosyth were blocked solid and motorists couldn't get off even if they wanted to. The police were sweating, trying to keep traffic moving, pushing broken down and punctured cars on to the grass verges. Cars overheated, or ran out of petrol and had to be towed to the nearest layby.

Crowds wait on the north span of the bridge to get a first glimpse of the Queen

The bridge itself was a solid mass four lanes of traffic inching forward, with people tossing coins out of their windows for luck. Many motorists who had come north over the bridge decided to return by Kincardine bridge, causing further bottlenecks on its approaches. Cowdenbeath was ten times busier than normal, a Crossgates woman was said to have waited twenty minutes to get across the road, and police were on points duty in Dunfermline trying to control traffic to and from the motorway at Rosyth.

Jimmy Macdonald, of Lochgelly was one of the eight patrolmen who had an enormously difficult job to do. A miner, Jimmy had been made redundant when the Minto Pit closed. He saw an advert for bridge patrolmen and had two weeks to practise before the opening day. He was one of the first men to cross the completed bridge. Workmen were still putting finishing touches to the bridge and cables were lying about. The bridge master told him to go across and check that all was clear before the traffic began to cross.

The patrolmen had scooters, little mini-motorbikes which enabled them to get through thick traffic to the scene of an accident or breakdown on the bridge. That first day, they were kept busy till after ten at night.

On opening day, the police motorbikes were too big to get through the tightly packed rows of cars, so Jimmy and has fellow patrols had to run about, driving on the white line in the middle of the road, trying to keep the traffic flowing. Police were kept busy preventing people from walking across the bridge, because the pedestrian crossing was not yet open.

Patrolmen had to cross and re-cross the bridge constantly, checking for motorists in trouble, and contacting the breakdown squad. Phones were installed at fifty yard intervals and motorists fined thirty shillings plus a pound for every fifteen minutes they were stranded. Jimmy was in the middle of the bridge when the 'bigwigs' procession crossed, and people in the cars were throwing coins over the side of the bridge.

'It was like a wedding scramble,' he said, 'showers of coins.'

Because the bridge was so wide, the pennies didn't go into the water. The patrolmen had the job of picking them up, and they were allowed to keep them. The practice of throwing coins had to be stopped for safety reasons. Men were still working on the bridge and a penny dropped from a great height could cause severe injury. One coin sank a quarter of an inch into the deck of a boat.

Jimmy also worked as a toll collector and went on to become supervisor before he retired in 1979. The first person to pay the toll on that first day was J.A.K. Hamilton, the bridge's resident engineer. Motorists in private cars paid half a crown. One man who paid with a twenty pound note received one hundred and fifty nine half crowns in change.

Problems included people not having the right money, or enough money. One man handed Jimmy a pile of loose change and took off before he could be stopped. A check on the money found it to be a penny ha'penny short, so Jimmy made up the amount from his own pocket. It also included an odd penny which Jimmy did not recognise so he put it in his pocket and replaced it with one of his own. Later he discovered the odd coin was a half sovereign. But that was all in the future and on the opening day, all those who worked on the bridge were concerned only that everything would go well.

And it did. if there were any hiccups, they were well and truly hidden. STV was credited with having the best coverage of the event, in spite of the fog. and their film was shot 'from the rail bridge, nearly a mile away.' There were mixed feelings about the day, as one reporter put it:

The sheer frustration of a forty mile crawl along approach roads evaporated by the magnificent experience of driving across the bridge. I was struck by a sense of pride and awe. Pride to be one of the first

The last voyage of the Sir William Wallace

74

to cross and awe at the magnificence of the structure itself... I caught an occasional glimpse of the rail bridge through the swirling fog, its cantilevers seeming huge and clumsy compared to the graceful lines of the newcomer.

Most of the cars from the north were not going to Edinburgh but travelling up the first slipway and joining the queue back to Fife. People came from Aberdeen just to cross, then turn round and go home again. One man made five return jouneys. Asked if he was trying to create some kind of record he replied that it was a marvellous bridge and because he couldn't stop on it, he wanted to get a really good look at it.

The huge flow of traffic took everyone by surprise. No-one was prepared. The bridge master said, *'We never expected anything like this. At this rate, the bridge is already too small.'*

The Daily Mail's motoring correspondent took an hour and ten minutes to cross the bridge. He wrote that it was expected that a two dual lane carriageway would be adequate until the 1980s, with a traffic flow of around five million vehicles a year. From the opening on Friday evening, till midnight on Sunday, more than eighty thousand vehicles crossed the bridge. A flow of around eleven million, which could be estimated from this number, would not be maintained but even with normal traffic, it was assumed a third motor lane each side would be needed in much less than fifteen years.

It was not the bridge that was at fault however.

Everyone was united in admiration for a stupendous feat of engineering. The sole reason for the traffic problem was considered to be the tolls. Writing in The Daily Mail, Dr Alan Thompson claimed that it took him one and a half hours to travel from Dunfermline to the outskirts of Edinburgh.

What I have seen tonight has fully convinced me that the principle of tolls on a major highway is an utter absurdity. As far as the Forth Bridge is concerned, it has resulted in obstruction and chaos.

He denied that traffic was abnormal, that what seemed so now would be normal in two years time, and called for an immediate abolition of tolls.

It is a tragedy that the achievement of engineers and scientists who have built the most streamlined and modern bridge in Europe has been sabotaged by an insistence on an obsolete method of toll collection.

On the whole, however, the newspapers made the most of this once in a lifetime occasion with photographs of the Queen, in her car; shaking hands with various dignitaries; surrounded by ranks of soldiers and sailors; with pipe and brass bands; and meeting the men who built the bridge. The ferry was not forgotten. *Tears From Crew As Last Ferry Moves Off*, ran one headline. *Sirens blasted a requiem as the last Forth Ferry faded into gathering fog of South Queensferry last night, while ferrymen and onlookers wept openly on the quay.* For some ferrymen, there was no time for tears. They had to change into their uniforms for a new job collecting tolls.

BRIDGE MEMORIES

The coming of the Forth Bridge was universally welcomed. Merchants and business men on both sides of the river expected a steady upsurge in trade. The economy of the country would flourish, tourism would increase as large parts of the Highlands would now be more easily accessible.

For the men who worked on the ferries, however, the building of the bridge meant a complete change of lifestyle and an end of generations of tradition. They accepted the necessity, but regretted the passing of a way of life that had existed for centuries.

Among those whose lives were changed by the bridge was Jim Hepburn. He had been a pier boy before becoming a deck hand on the ferries before the war started in 1939. He recalled the German raid on the Forth when enemy planes were shot down and their crews captured.

'It was pretty scary. We had no protection. Some people thought that the plane was back firing, then we realised that it was machine guns...'

Ferry boats were tied up during the raid, but later that night, Jim's boat transported some of the prisoners across the river on their way to Edinburgh Castle.

'They were all young boys,' he said, 'about seventeen or eighteen, and scared out of their wits what would happen to them.'

Skippers ran a normal service throughout the war and had to cope with wind, tide and fog as well as occasionally being overloaded with tanks and guns. One day a mine bobbed up under the bridge and the deck hands had to push it away with oars.

After the war, with the increase in road traffic, the *Mary Queen of Scots* was introduced and Jim was relief mate during holiday periods. The crossing time was seven and a half minutes in summertime, and it took twenty minutes to load forty cars and passengers, who sometimes had to wait more than two hours to get across.

When the *Sir William Wallace* came into service, Jim was made skipper, along with John Penny, but even with the new ships, the ferry service couldn't cope. They watched the new bridge taking shape and knew the end was near. Jim particularly remembered one night.

'It was blowing a gale and the ferry was closed because they thought the north pillar was going to come down. I didn't have stays on it at the time and was swaying fourteen feet in the wind.'

Jim was on the last boat to cross on the night before the bridge opened. He had to get a train across to Dalmeny to be on the tolls when the traffic started to cross about five in the afternoon.

The four ferry boats were taken to Burntisland docks and lay there for a year. The *Sir William Wallace* went to the bulb fields in Holland, the others were scrapped.

Like the other ferrymen, Jim was given a job collecting tolls on the new bridge but he only stuck it for about six months.

'I wasn't used to handling money and you were getting half crowns thrown at you, drivers not knowing what to do. It was claustrophobic in the tolls after being outside all day.'

Steven Reid worked for fourteen years on the ferries from 1951 when he came out of the army to the last day of the last day of the Queensferry Passage.

'I worked as a pierman till a vacancy for a deckhand arose, then as an after end deck hand. That was straightforward, just throwing the rope for the boat to be tied up. After that I moved to the forward deck and got more capstan work coming in to the pier. The pierman's job was to catch the rope, make the boat fast and direct the traffic. We had an average of thirty six to thirty eight cars on the boat and the pierman had to check lorries, buses and cars and organise the loading to balance the boat. You wanted a nice straight line of cars.

The deck hand looked after and controlled the traffic loading and unloading, and the mate guided vehicles to the bow or stern. The skipper's responsibility was getting the boat from one side to the other so the only time he was involved with traffic was when the mate was on a lunch or tea break There was also an engineer and a clerkess who sold tickets from an office on the boat.

I was mate for three years, then skipper for the last five years on the *Robert The Bruce*, which was, incidentally, the first all welded boat to be built in Britain. Before the traffic began to increase you could stand on the pier on a winter night and not see a single car. You'd come in empty and go out empty. As traffic began to build up you had a full load from first run in the morning at six forty five till the last one at night, eleven in winter half past eleven in summer.

I remember the good weather best. The easterly wind was worst with a swell coming up the river. The south shore was rocky and shallow, so if you had any wind at all, you had to be careful or you'd be there till the tide turned. Fog was always a problem. We had no radar, just a compass but the wheelhouse was so small there was no room for a binnacle so the compass hung from the roof.

You blew the whistle when you left the pier and if no ships answered, you ran full speed for twelve minutes, then slowed down and felt our way in with the help of the foghorn. Once when the foghorn broke down, a pierman rattled with his spanner on the pier to guide us in.

On the day the bridge was opened, two navy ships with radar and powerful engines bumped into each other. When the Queen crossed the bridge, there was still stuff lying about, so though she officially closed the ferries, we had to keep running till the bridge opened.

Most of the ferry men came from North Queensferry, and though the bridge brought increased prosperity to most of Fife, the changes to North Queensferry were disastrous. While the ferries were running, there were streams of visitors, many coming from Edinburgh for Sunday afternoon outings.

Madge Stobbie recalled there being lots of shops, two doctors and a police station. Her husband, Jock, was born and brought up in North Queensferry and she has lived in the village for over sixty years. While the bridge was being built, she had a series of lodgers, men working on different stage of the construction.

Jock Stobbie was a shot firer, placing explosive charges in tunnels and shafts being bored on the north side of the bridge, and blasting rocks in the Forth. A newspaper described him as handling submarine gelignite as if it were a stick of rock. He was among those present watching John Maclay, the Secretary of State for Scotland, drive the first pile of the new bridge at Port Edgar, South Queensferry on November 22nd, 1958.

It was one of four which would enable work to begin on the foundations of the tower supporting the southern approach.

For all the men who worked on the construction of the Forth Bridge, from the architects, designers and engineers to the steelmen, joiners, electricians and labourers doing hundreds of different jobs, there is a common thread that runs through their story. It is the enormous pride and satisfaction in having been a part of such a stunning production. At the time, some were aware of the magnitude of the operation; to others it was just a job, sometimes difficult and uncomfortable, but extremely well paid. Jim Sinclair, a diver, had just returned from the Persian Gulf and was living in Glasgow when he got a phone call from John Howard and Company saying they needed a chief diver to start work on the foundations of the bridge.

A huge figure of eight steel pile frame had been erected and had to be towed into position, then

Boring in preparation for clearing rocks

lowered on to the sea bed. Coffer dams were built of sheet steel and the problem was that when the water was pumped out, the piles might be pressed inward by pressure from sea water outside.

The divers' job was to build the dam inside the piles so that it would not collapse.

Most of this work was done virtually in complete darkness, everything done by touch because there was

Getting ready to dive

little visibility. The sea was very mucky. One of the jobs, where I nearly lost my life, compressed air was being pumped down to the diver. The pump actually stopped so I was under water with no air, but I managed to get back to the surface.

There were two divers working on the sea bed, with two linesmen looking after them and the telephone line, and one looking after the compressor. One section was quite difficult. We were fixing eighteen foot strongbolts to keep the section firm and one diver had to stand on the other's shoulders to put in the top bolts.

It was hard work and bad weather didn't stop the diving. On the north side, we dived at night in coffer dams sheltered from the weather. Our part of the project lasted about six months altogether. Once the dams were pumped out, the engineers could go in and start the work of constructing the towers.

When the foundations for the north pier were being excavated, the remains of an iron ship were discovered. Jimmy Hutchinson was working at Rosyth Dockyard, in charge of a motor fishing vessel, known as the diving boat. Marine salvage divers were used to dealing with wrecks, so the diving boat was tied up against the coffer dam and Royal Navy divers went down to inspect it.

Their equipment was more sophisticated than that used by Jim Sinclair and his colleagues, but even for them working conditions were grim. The water was icy cold and it was pitch black because the stirred up mud was like black ink. Heat cutting equipment was used and the wreck broken up. Part of the hull was lifted clear but there were no means of identification. The remainder was towed further out away from the working area.

Jim Taylor worked on the bridge foundations, starting as a bulldozer driver excavating the cable tunnels.

'We saw what was going on in the coffer dams, the drilling and boring through whinstone. Most of the rock was brought out through pumping. When the anchorage tunnels were complete, I got paid off, but got taken on by Whatlings, and kept in touch with the men building the bridge. When they started putting the floor of the bridge together it was really frightening.

The riggers, erecters and welders were all working together and they didn't have much safe place to stand while the huge box girder beams were being swung into place. The crane would pick up the beams and swing them out and the men who didn't need to be there disappeared. They were always on about safety, really strict. People didn't like the safety rules but they complied.

Men learned to improvise. The winch house was a wooden box with no heating, so they got a big block of wood with a brass fitting, put a 250 watt bulb in it, then put a tin can with holes in it over the bulb. That was their winter heating.

Tom Gibson started working on the bridge in 1961 when he was nineteen and left two or three months before the opening day.

'I was working for Redpath Brown, Structural Engineers in Edinburgh and was told that projects like the bridge were the place to make money. I got a job and never looked back, found I could take it in my stride. My first job was carrying bags of thousands of bolts to the workshop, where they were stripped down, cleaned and oiled before use. It was boring, but I got promoted to carrying the bolts up to where they were needed.

I was very lucky being so young – I was probably the youngest person employed on the construction – to

...and going down

work with such experienced workmen. It served me well the rest of my life. The quality of the men was outstanding and it was a great pleasure seeing the bridge come together. Even the women working in the canteen took pride in it, everyone was proud to be a part of it.

I worked with the cranes as a banksman, connecting the chains to the burden rope of the crane. That part I really enjoyed, it was an essential part of the work. There was no formal training, if you showed an aptitude for something, that's what you did. What really mattered was having confidence in yourself and others around you.

The majority of the men had experience in the merchant navy or on whaling ships, so were used to working with lashings and wire ropes, used to inclement weather and knew how to deal with it. They didn't have the safety restrictions they do now, and we worked about a sixty hour week. There were times when things went badly wrong but that was seen as an acceptable part of the job. One Sunday morning, a sailor's body was found where they were sinking the main shaft for the piers. Port Edgar was open then and apparently sailors would climb over the catwalks to get back to HMS Cochrane.

The worst accident was when they were dismantling the safety nets after construction was completed. Three men were killed. Usually accidents were minor, broken arms and so on. One man fell off the safety net into the water south of the main tower. A pilot boat was coming in to land and the man jumped in to save him, but got into difficulties and the guy who fell in had to help him back into the boat.

Helmets were compulsory but apart from that, it was up to you. Most of the men wore army issue tank suits because of the wind. One winter was horrendous, with snow and ice and very low temperatures for a very long time. They had to use steam heaters so they could mix concrete. People didn't mind the cold, it was the wind they didn't like.

Spinning was a very complicated business and the

Working inside the coffer dams before pumping...

spinners had to keep going. It wasn't really spinning, the wires were laid parallel then wrapped and tightly packed. It was a very involved and difficult job, working on a steep incline. The suspenders that held the deck, each one had to be tested, and painted after it was done.

The man who built the cages tested them personally and he was about twenty stone. The steel was brought from Drem to the railway siding at South Queensferry. The old oil tanks used by the navy were adapted to use as stores. The steel was then taken to the jetty and lifted up from there. When we were working on the deck, the only way to get from the ground to deck level was by what was called the muck buckets which were lifted by the derricks. You had to be fit to manoeuvre your way from bucket to deck and vice versa.

Anyone who complained about conditions was told to go and get a job in Woolies. As the deck crept out, ladders were set up. When the final section was fitted, it had all been carefully measured and fitted precisely.

Ronnie Bedburgh worked for three and a half years on the bridge, starting as a fitter's mate.

'I worked with the erectors and covered the whole of the bridge, suspenders and cables, and had to go up ladders to the sheaves that carried the cables. I worked on the north side and had to travel from South Queensferry every day in a little boat. It was a bit hairy at times in rough weather.

The wire men were in the same spot eight hours a day and the highest tea boy in Britain carried tea and hot soup on his back. I was on every part of the steel work. The catwalks were safe but the back of your legs hurt it was so steep and bounced up and down all the time. You would be bent double against the wind, and sometimes there would be fog on the ground but bright sunshine at the top of the towers. It was so high up there, the seagulls were flying below you. It was interesting watching the spinning being done. It's hard to believe that thousands of tons are floating on that every day and no-one gives it a second thought.

...and after all the water has been pumped out

On the day the bridge opened, the thousands of people who gathered to watch the ceremony were unaware of the frantic activity that had been going on all night. Lindsay Tait tells the story.

'It seemed an ordinary day at work. On Wednesday, September 3rd, 1964, my mate Jimmy Devine and I were working on yet another mundane job in Dunfermline as a cable jointing team with the South of Scotland Electricity Board. It was a bright sunny day and there was a buzz in the air as preparations were being finalised for the visit of the Queen to open the Forth Bridge next day. We had worked on and off in Queensferry during the construction of the bridge as new electricity stations had to be installed to feed the bridge. We had watched it rise from the River Forth to what was now a majestic new landmark.

At about four o'clock, our foreman arrived at the site to say there was a fault in one of the high tensile cables feeding the bridge and the construction camp at the bottom of the main bridge support. We were soon on our way to Queensferry to sort out the problem, hopefully before the Queen arrived. The cable fault was located in the water on one of the jetties that had been constructed to reach out to the main pillars in the Forth.

The contractors were not happy as their power supplies were off, and last minute jobs were being held up. The team got going and we knew we would have to spend many hours on to jetty to repair the fault.

As the hours passed, and night drew on, the swell on the water grew and it was like working in a shower. It also got very cold after midnight but we worked on against a deadline, watched by very anxious contractors who kept asking how long it would be before the job was finished. Well, we did finish, the power was back on at six, but by the time we were cleaned up and all the testing completed it was half past nine. We had been at work without rest for twenty six hours, and breakfast and a good sleep seemed to beckon.

At home in Crossgates I was rudely awakened by a flight of RAF jets as they roared down the main street heading for the bridge, which the Queen had just opened. Although tired, I felt proud that the lads from SSEB, Halbeath, had saved part of the day and that the lights shining along the length of the bridge that night was a reward for a very long and busy shift.'

In an enormous steel and concrete structure like the bridge, it may seem strange that joiners have a very important part to play.

Joiners Campbell Morris, Arthur Slater and Alexander Tarvit all had experience of huge concrete structures. Arthur, from Banffshire had worked on Hydro-electric schemes, at Cluanie Dam and Invermoriston, and came to Fife with the promise of a job and a house in Glenrothes. Campbell and Alexander worked at Kincardine Power Station, at Westfield and on buildings such as the tower block of the Victoria Hospital in Kirkcaldy.

The joiners were a small team, maybe eight or ten men in two squads with a foreman and two charge hands, part of the workforce of Howards who had the contracts for the foundations and anchorages. Later Alex and Arthur were employed by Reed and Mallik, on the structure of the piers supporting the viaducts.

The joiners job on the bridge was to construct the shuttering which was used as a framework for the concrete and they were involved in many aspects of the foundation work, cable tunnels, coffer dams and towers.

'We worked under the engineers. They designed the job and sometimes they knew best, but they depended on our experience.

The anchorage tunnel on the north side was a hundred and seventy six feet long and had to be blasted out of earth and solid rock.

When the tunnel was driven, there were patches of bad rock, and nets had to be placed under the roof to prevent injury from falling rocks.

We made timber frames for the concrete arches which had to be put in position to support the roof before the concreting could be done. Once the anchorages and cables were in position, there was a shaft at the back of the twin tunnels where the cable ends were fixed to the anchors. We had to go down in a bucket. It was like a pit shaft, about six feet wide. You made the shuttering, which was erected in sections.

For the coffer dams, the divers went down and made a rough sketch of the rock to enable the joiners to build a frame to as near the right size as possible. After the framework for the coffer dams was floated out into place, the divers went down and made a rough sketch of the rock. We made a frame to as near the right size as possible and made adjustments as necessary.

Steel piles were laid on the Mackintosh Rock, we built shutters inside them and the space between was filled with rock and stones before the concrete was pumped in. This was done by putting pipes with holes in them all the way round and the concrete was hosed into them.

The dams were what you called clutch piled, fixed in a kind of Greek key pattern and piles were sealed with red lead paste. That wasn't a hundred per cent successful and water would come in, just a trickle but it had to be sealed.

The tower construction is complete

Ash was brought from the paper mills and two men had a steady job checking for leaks and pouring ash. The sea water washed it into the space to seal the cracks.

You could tell when a ship was coming up the Forth because more water would be squirting in.

Sea cocks were built into the piles in case the water pressure became too high. Only once can I remember having to open them sea cocks, and we had to abandon the dam. There was an unusually high tide with a gale coming straight across from the Bo'ness side. And the water was right over the causeway.

We had to get a lorry to take us off. The next morning, our trestles and battens of wood were hanging in among the steel. The dam had to be pumped out and cleaned again. Once the foundation for the towers were laid, the work of building began.

The towers consisted of two reinforced concrete legs and a cross beam, and were built in sections. The walls are two foot thick and hollow, with a floor every thirty feet. Construction was carried out using a climbing tower crane in each leg. The joiners worked on scaffolding hung on what was called a cathead frame, which could be raised by hydraulic jack.

The scaffolding was held only by two bolts, something they were always very much aware of. It was lifted with them on it. Alexander remembered one incident when the platform came loose.

'After the arch was built, they had a special crane on top and the first lift, it didn't have enough power to lift the shuttering, so when the bolts were taken out, the whole thing dropped. I jumped off the shutter on to the corbel – that was a kind of ridge or shelf on the side of the tower, but the tower itself started shaking.'

Arthur pulled him back on to the platform again. Working high was not a problem but Campbell didn't like working above the water.

Joiners dismantling the shuttering

'You had to anchor all your tools to your body. If you dropped anything that was it. Not everyone on the team could swim, but it probably wouldn't matter anyway, if you fell in. When we started on the curve of the arch that was the worst bit because the weight was all to one side.

The only time anyone wore safety harness was when they were working on the arch. Sometimes it was so frosty that you couldn't see the ground below you and your oilskin jacket would be white with frost.

Shuttering was made from fifty millimetre tongue and groove battens. It had to be placed perfectly because you couldn't tell if it was right or not till the concrete was poured and the battens removed. The concrete had retardants added so that it wouldn't stick to the wood, which was used over and over again.

It was just a job to us. We were there because we could earn good money. You worked all hours, they'd come to you just as you were finishing up, and ask you to lie on. It was unusual to get a night off – but that was the way the system worked.

When we were doing a pouring, we'd be working from six in the morning till midnight. Everything depended on concrete. We worked on one leg of the tower, then the other, time about. When we were putting in the last pour of concrete on top of the tower, there were reporters there. One asked if we knew we were making history.

'History's no use to me,' Jimmy Wishart told him, 'I can't go to the grocers and say here's some history, give me a pound of sugar.'

After the main towers were finished, we moved on to the side towers and the piers supporting the road. There were some funny incidents. The crane dropped a beam and divers went down to find it, but it had disappeared completely. It must have swung out into the river and got buried in silt. However, not long after, the lineman dropped his false teeth and the diver went

A corennie granite panel

down and picked them out of the mud. Another time, the line man was letting the diver down when he overbalanced and he passed the diver on the way down.

There were problems with the concrete if it got too cold, so at one time, there was a liner in dry dock at Inverkeithing, waiting to be broken up. All the mattresses from the cabins were brought in as protection from frost.

One of our jobs was making Corennie granite panels. These covered the bases of the side towers and viaduct piers and the main piers below water level. To begin with we used Polycell adhesive paste mixed with crushed granite but it took a long time to dry and required careful handling. Any vibration and the stones, which were set in place individually, would slip. Later, we used hardwall plaster and crushed granite which was more efficient.

What most of the men working on the bridge remember is the cameraderie. They needed to be able to depend on each other and worked as a team. Dave Melville and Les Wood didn't begin work on the bridge till 1962, building shutters for concrete slabs for the part of the bridge carrying the road from the viaduct to the main towers.

In stormy weather, things had to be lashed down, and the wind was the worst thing they had to deal with.

Though they didn't feel the motion too much, Dave realised how much the bridge moved when he took a sight line on the rail bridge. They worked twelve hour shifts and the standard gear was tank suits.

While they watched the decking reaching out across the river, it seemed unlikely that the two sections would meet exactly in the middle, but of course they did and the

The north-west anchorage chamber

last section was bedecked with flags. Then, as they were not making history, it was off to the next big job.

Davie Lockhart's memories of the bridge are rather different from the workers. In the fifties he was an art teacher inDunfermline.

' In the days before comprehensive education, three boys in Queen Anne Junior Secondary School, with enormous effort, skill and ingenuity, achieved something which ought to have earned them lasting credit and even an introduction to the queen. They created the Forth Road Bridge in 1957, seven years before it was built.

As assistant teacher of art at the beginning of the summer term, I had a pleasant, valuable but problem class of twelve boys of an hour and twenty minutes each week. The class was not the problem - twelve boys in 1957 was luxury teaching and the individuals were pleasant youngsters of great goodwill.

With a comprehensive set of equipment I was training the boys to do printing for the school - but it was based on a little Adana platen printing press. I could usefully employ about eight of the lads at any given time but the rest would be spectators.

One morning as the class was entering, three boys approached excitedly bearing a newspaper whose front page announced that the long sought after road bridge over the Forth was to be built. An architect's visualisation accompanied this article.

"See that, sir, they're gonnae build the brig", cried the boys. We scanned the sheet together and a memory came sharply to me. Nine years previously, while employed in the studio of an Edinburgh sculptor, I had witnessed a large scale model of a road bridge being made.

The model, which was the length of the large studio, was of a half mile bridge to be built over a highland glen traversed by two or three streams, and it was set on a copy of the terrain. I told the boys about

Joiners on the scaffolding platform

it and the boys, needing no prompting, demanded that we 'do' the new Forth Bridge.

'We'd need long straps of wood and board of some kind,' I demurred, 'and plans from the engineers.'

'The engineers' names are in the paper,' said the boys, 'ye can write tae them.'

'No I won't, you will do all the writing necessary - it will come better from you.'

There was no hesitation, the boys were alight.

'And where do we get the materials?' I asked, but that had already been resolved.

'There's a big project board in the jannie's place. There's all we would need there.'

'Away and write your letter then,' I said and turned back to the printers. Barely twenty minutes elapsed before they were back. Their letter was brief and brilliant, I could not have done better myself.

The bulky envelope of plans arrived from Mott, Hay and Anderson in time for our next session and the boys lost no time in retrieving the lathe-framed nine foot square of beaver board. The boys took the scale plan's dimension, worked out the maximum size possible for their model and the old project panel was stripped and ready for assembly before they left for their next class.

From then on, the boys worked almost independently, just encouraged by me. I could not neglect my printers. I acted really as a consultant throughout, the boys did the work.

They did need help with problems of materials like plaster, wire and such, but the boys were the problem solvers from time to time and spectacularly so. Then disaster struck.

Only painting and some detail remained to be done when we arrived one morning to see that the carriageways of wood had warped and all the carefully tensioned condenser - wire supporting the cables had slackened. Our work was in ruins. There's nothing anyone can do when wood warps like that.

Alan Bennett, Robert Somerville and Ernest Girdler work on their model

'We could get mair wid,' the boys pleaded. 'And start again.'

'There isn't time', I said, but they had made me work with them after school and on Saturdays for weeks and were not giving up. They retired to contemplate their ruined work and ten minutes later I was summoned.

The model was restored, even improved. Its length had been centred on two stools and with one boy bearing down on each end the structure tautened to the right form.

'See,' said the boys, 'you said it was finished but we've got it to the right form.'

'All right,' I said, ' We'll just cart it round Scotland with you two hanging on to the ends.' (*There was already talk about taking the model on tour.*)

The boys were almost pitying me. 'No, sir, there's two straps of wood left, well nail them along the sides while it's held in this position.'

A teacher's ultimate success. The boys had thought it all through, solved the problem and had secured the solution. The bridge was finished in time, and Mott, Hay and Andersen was promptly informed. Two of their people came to the school and were impressed to the point of being shaken. They pointed out council houses alongside an abandoned railway under the bridge at South Queensferry.

'You're showing these houses there,' they exclaimed, 'we've not yet been able to decide whether some will have to be demolished or not - perhaps well be able to consult your model.'

It was then that I offended against public relations. A prominent local journalist connected to a great national newspaper wanted to take the model round the principal towns of Scotland. He telephoned me to make arrangements. With all the months of effort and skill in my mind, I demanded £1000 for the school's funds. The journalist dropped his idea like a hot brick; I know a request for £20 might well have been acceptable but I felt that I was not seeking charity but something reflecting the real value of the work as it stood. The headmaster never forgave me.

Ernest puts the finishing touches to the project

Summer vacation intervened. I accepted a transfer to another school in the county. The model was proudly installed in the foyer of the City Chambers and that was that.

When the bridge was completed in 1964, preparations were being made for a grand opening ceremony to be performed by the Queen. It occurred right away to me that the model of the bridge might be of interest somewhere for the occasion. I set about discovering where it might have ended up.

No one knew anything about it, and no one wanted to know. I believe that, after gathering dust in the foyer for a few weeks or so it had been consigned by philistines unknown and unknowing to some local dump. In fairness be it said that the model was fragile and might not have survived being handled by the insensitive.'

There is a sequel to Davie's story. He remembered the surname of one of the boys and found the name in the phone book. He was saddened to hear that Ernest Girdler had died, but was delighted to be speaking to Ernest's widow, who had heard the story many times from her husband and mother in law.

Penny Girdler not only knew the story but still had the photographs and press articles which appeared on July 3, 1957.

The photographer who took these pictures was Morris Allan. He had a long and adventurous relationship with the bridge.

'My earliest photos were taken when I went to record the old ferry queues waiting to drive through North Queensferry to the pier. It was calculated that if the queue reached a certain spot at Ferryhills, you were as quick to go round by Kincardine as to wait for the ferry. I had worked for the Dunfermline and West Fife Journal, but was mostly involved in taking photos for national newspapers.

The Bulletin, which was *the* picture paper for Glasgow, had staff photographers in Edinburgh but a trip across the Forth could take an hour and a half so it was simpler for them to employ me.

Though there was opposition to tolls in some quarters, most of the people crossing every day felt that tolls would not be any higher than ferry charges. The bridge was seen as the most magnificent silver ribbon of freedom across the river. A bit of history was happening under my nose and I knew I'd regret it if I didn't record it, so decided to make a monthly trip to some given point, probably somewhere near North Queensferry Station.

What I didn't realise was the amount of preliminary work that had to be done at ground level and below, but every month one of us, that is myself or the two photographers I employed at the time would make the trip. Once they started spinning the cables from north to south , making a spiders web across the Forth, the whole conception of a photographer's eye view changed.

Fine cables were taken across the river and a walkway constructed, not one with a solid floor just wire mesh. Basically it was like a chicken coop turned on its side. I had to go up there to get the kind of pictures I wanted. I wanted a record of the building of the towers with the saddling on top which was to hold the cables.

It was relatively simple to get up. There was a rocky promontory almost on the level of what would be the roadway, but getting on to the walkways was like going out into space.

I was aware that this was going to be a historic building but couldn't see how it would beat the attractiveness of the rail bridge. However it was going to be a very important structure in Scottish commercial life, linking Fife with the rest of Scotland.

Because of this, I had decided to take photos on a fairly large format press camera using 5x4 inch negatives. The advantage of this was that it could be used in all weathers, being designed for use at sporting events and royal visits where you had to get pictures even if it was blowing a gale. The equipment was very heavy but we were accustomed to carrying stuff around. However, carrying it on terra firma was one thing, carrying it on a walkway when you could look down and see nothing beneath you but the Forth was quite different.

I always had the feeling that my feet were going to go through the mesh instead of staying on the surface. You are supposed to keep a hand on the safety rail but you can't do that if you have to manoeuvre a camera, change negatives and so on. It was not easy and occasionally pictures suffered from camera shake.

The men who worked up there moved around like flies. When I approached the site engineer for permission, he was not too happy. I was allowed to go ahead on the understanding that it was at my own risk and their insurance certainly wouldn't cover me. I told him I'd been on top of the rail bridge when I'd done a feature on a week in the life of a painter on the bridge.

It had been an interesting experience but it was fairly solid with a walkway beside the railway line and little shelters you could duck into when a train came along.

Morris trying to keep a steady hand

I was very careful not to cause the workmen any concern about my safety, so I tried to behave as if I did this every day of my life. They thought I was mad and treated me like the tea boy.'

'Have you been up here before son?' they asked. I was quite small and they were all big men but they were all very helpful and were pleased to have photos of themselves at work – not something that happened very often, I suppose.

One day I was coming back across the catwalk to the north tower. It was bucketing rain and thunder, and though I didn't see any lightning I couldn't help thinking that this was the biggest lightning conductor for miles around. The men were scooging as they called it, sheltering from the rain and have cups of tea from syrup tin billy cans.

I always took a flask of tea with me because I couldn't see myself going down off the bridge for a cup of tea and then going back up again. One of the problems was that if you did go away, it was difficult to find the same spot again because the miles of walkways looked the same.

We had a chat about how difficult it was to keep dry when the wind was whipping the rain up the Forth and you could feel the salt spray even a hundred and fifty feet above the sea.

At times it felt more like a thousand feet. Walkways wouldn't sag with your weight, but with their own. When they started swaying you got to thinking 'Well if the camera case goes over , too bad. I'm hanging on.' Sometimes you had to cross from one walkway to another by means of crossways and, though it might only have been about a hundred yards

there and back, it was like a day's work on your nerves.

From a photographer's point of view you'd sometimes find a picture that was perfect. One day, the suspender ropes had a harp like appearance with the early morning frost and the sun hitting them.

One day, I was taking photographs on the hillside above what is now the Admiralty Roundabout, where I could get a bird's eye view of the work being carried out on the approach roads. One of Whatling's drivers wanted to know what I was doing there. I think he believed I was an industrial spy, but then I was asked to do progress reports on all the work they were doing in Fife.

One job was for an undersea tunnel taking pipes for North Sea gas to Methil power station. I thought that would be an easier job than the bridge but it turned out to be taking pictures of the progress of a six by five foot tunnel carrying gas to the Lurgi plant at Westfield. So I have the distinction of being a hundred and fifty feet above the Forth and about the same depth under it. It was not the nicest of places. I've never been keen on underground though I've done many mining pictures. Watching the bridge develop and recording each stage in it journey was a unique and rewarding experience, just as the bridge itself is unique.

On the opening day, I was asked by STV to take centre position on the centre span of the bridge and take film of the royal car driving across, turning at the end and coming back. I had a sixteen millimetre camera and a specially built platform and we were ordered by the police not to move from this position.

However, when we heard an awful clang we had to go and look. A ship had hit the bridge but it was so misty we couldn't see anything, but there were no shouts of alarm so we assumed everything was okay. The fog had lifted a little by the time the Queen arrived but we couldn't get a proper picture. Through the mist we saw the Royal Standard and got a glimpse of a glossy limousine, but never even saw the Queen.

I wasn't sorry that I hadn't been assigned to film the formal opening because each royal visit has a certain pattern. I had met most of the Royals and was particularly impressed by the Queen Mother. I met her on many occasions and she always greeted me and my colleagues by name. I couldn't control the weather though, which was a shame because I had nurtured that bridge since it was a gleam in the designer's eye. Now here it was – the climax, the royal opening – and what do I get? A shot of the royal flag.'

A floodlit bridge and a sparkling Fife in the background

Since last we sent our Christmas cheer, a new arrival has come here.
To build the Bridge the boys won't fail as Judy joins them, in a pail.
Nova Scotia's future's in good hands, we send to all of you
The happiest Season's Greetings now, and Good Luck for 'Sixty-Two!

This Allan family Christmas card caused considerable consternation when it appeared in 1961

INTO THE FUTURE

While the Forth Bridge was being built, other world shaking events were taking place. The fifties saw the birth of the teenager, the first generation of young people who had money, freedom and a new identity and culture of their own. They were the days of Teddy Boys, Cliff Richard and rock and roll, Bill Haley and Tommy Steele, frothy coffee and skiffle groups. The first long playing records and stereo music was introduced, and the hovercraft was invented. Elvis was drafted into the army, people joined CND and went on Ban The Bomb marches.

In 1958, seven Busby Babes died in the Munich air disaster, along with eleven others; the last debutantes appeared at Buckingham Palace; the first bubble car was shown at the motor show and parking meters were introduced in London. Iraq still had a king, Feisal, who was on a state visit to London with his son.

By the sixties, the country was coming to an end of thirteen years of Tory government. Harold Wilson was poised to take over, George Brown planned to tackle the problems of 'Britain's lop sided economy' and the Communist Party were putting up thirty six candidates.

Beatlemania was in full flood, and *Steptoe and Son* top of the television ratings; there was a state of emergency in Malaysia, and the Warren Commission Report into the killing of President Kennedy was published. A woman climbed the Eiger, the Mini was launched, the first motorway opened and Britain and France agreed to build the channel tunnel.

People in Fife were concerned with more mundane things, specifically whether or not tolls should be levied on the new bridge. The arguments had been going on as long as the bridge was in progress. When John McLay, the Secretary of State for Scotland, announced in parliament at the beginning of 1957, that agreement had been reached for the bridge to go ahead, he said that, as announced earlier, government loans would be repaid from the proceeds of tolls.

He insisted that toll systems were not obsolete, that many were in existence in Europe and America. Arthur Woodburn, the Labour member for Clackmannan and East Stirlingshire, welcomed the Minister's statement and added that once the bridge was built, we could easily get rid of the tolls.

Dunfermline's Provost John Allan complained that this was an entirely new procedure in Government financial policy and it had been strenuously opposed by the Forth Road Bridge Joint Board. The bridge would form part of the trunk road system of the country and the charging of tolls in those circumstances seemed unwarranted.

In February 1963, newspapers announced the failure of the No-Tolls campaign, but dissatisfaction continued. In August that year, Willie Hamilton, MP for West Fife was blaming uncertainty about the amount of tolls to be charged, for delays in new industries setting up in Donibristle. The answer to all complaints was that the choice had always been a toll bridge, or no bridge at all.

Despite the arguments which, forty years on, still erupt from time to time with greater or lesser, there was never any shortage of people willing to pay the crossing fee. From the original cost of half a crown (12½ new pence), it increased to eighty pence in 1986 and is due to become one pound in October 2004.

The completion of the bridge ended one stage of the project, and marked the beginning of another. The bridge master and his team have to constantly monitor and maintain the fabric, which over the years, has been subject to colossal strains, because of the ever increasing volume of traffic. When the bridge was designed in the 1950s, the heaviest lorries weighed twenty four tons, compared to today's standard weight of forty four tonnes. In forty years, traffic volume has increased sixfold, tailbacks of several miles are daily occurrences and bottlenecks occur on all approach road junctions.

Maintenance work can cause disruption to traffic, but consultation takes place with adjacent authorities,

The coffer dam construction

the Scottish Executive, the emergency services and user groups to minimise the impact. The actual structure of the bridge has had to be upgraded to ensure that the towers could cope with the extra weight generated by current and expected traffic loads.

New steel columns one hundred and forty metres high, and capable of withstanding loads of six thousand tons, were constructed inside each of the main towers' two legs. This work took two years and used sixteen hundred tonnes of steel, most of which was slid into the tower at river level. It was then jacked up inside the hollow structure.

Defences were also constructed round the legs of the main towers to minimise the impact of a collision by shipping, a risk which had not been considered in the original design. River traffic is a hazard to all such bridges and whilst the risk of collision was thought to be minimal, studies indicated that a ship colliding with one of the highly stressed towers could cause considerable damage before being halted by the towers.

Several options were considered and a cellular coffer dam formation chosen, because of the relative ease and speed of this form of construction. Built on the navigation side of each pier, the protection consisted of interlocked coffer dam constructions, built of steel and filled with crushed rock and capped with concrete.

Specialist marine plant, including dredgers, jack up rigs, crane barges and supply vessels were used but during the construction period, the thousands of drivers crossing the bridge every day were quite unaware of the activity going on below.

The work took longer than expected because of a combination of bad weather and difficult conditions but it was also hampered by the presence of the remains of a wreck on the sea bed. This iron ship was discovered when the coffer dams for the north pier were being built. Only part of it had been removed at that time and the remainder removed some distance away.

One aspect of this project was the consideration given to environmental issues and discussions were held with Scottish National Heritage. (SNH)

On the Long Craig Rock, close to the north pier, a colony of rare roseate terns breed every summer, so SNH requested that all construction work be done outwith the months of April to July. In fact it began in October 1996 and was completed in March 1998.

The management of the road bridge passed, in 2002, from the Forth Road Bridge Joint Board to the Forth Estuary Transport Authority (FETA), which has put forward a number of development plans. Although the original loans on the bridge were repaid, income from tolls is required to help pay for ever increasing maintenance costs. These include the continuing maintenance of the bridge, upgrading of the A8000 approach road, increasing the size of the Ferrytoll Park and Ride, and other improvements in public transport over the river.

The toll equipment is also in need of modernisation and FETA plan to introduce electronic collection equipment by 2006. This would enable charges to be lowered outside rush hours in order to encourage people to stagger journeys and reduce congestion at peak times. Though this automation will help speed traffic on its way, it will go only a little way to solve a problem which has been recognised from day one.

The difficulties encountered on opening day, though the circumstances were unique, showed the shortcomings as well as the benefits of the bridge.

'We never expected anything like this' said Robert Wilson, the Bridgemaster, *'At this rate the bridge is already too small.'*

In its first year, the bridge carried four million vehicles. By 2003, the number was over twenty four million and Bridgemaster Alastair Andrew reported a daily average of over thirty three thousand. Annual increases will serve only to exacerbate the problem. Improving the A8000 will reduce congestion on the bridge but will do little to reduce overall traffic growth.

The completed defences

It seems likely that by 2014, which will see the fiftieth anniversary of the bridge, plans will be well under way for a second Forth Bridge. FETA insists that by 2025, a new crossing will be essential. This is likely to generate as much discussion and arguments as the original did.

Plans for a new crossing at Queensferry were under discussion by the Scottish Office in the 1990s but were dropped by Labour after the 1997 election. In 2003, the Scottish Transport Minister Nicol Stephen recommended that FETA contact the consultants and ask them to review their findings, which would probably have to be updated bearing in mind the design code changes and the present day emphasis on a shift away from private to public transport.

Mike Rumney, Convenor of FETA argued that simply building another bridge would add to the congestion in east central Scotland. Any plan should be a part of the National Planning Framework, which is a blueprint of major projects that affect the country as a whole.

Several suggestions have been proposed, including a multi-modal bridge giving priority to public transport and capable of taking a light railway or tramline linking to Edinburgh's proposed tram system.

According to a Scottish Executive spokesman, however, they had no plans at present for another crossing and were working instead on measures to reduce traffic and congestion. Mike Rumney disagrees.

'The problem of congestion at the Forth Road bridge is not going to go away and it has a major impact on the economy of Scotland. It is essential that pressure is brought to bear on ministers to understand the key strategic significance of a third crossing for the benefit of Scotland as a whole.'

But there are doubts. History has a way of repeating itself. In the thirties, the erection of the Kincardine Bridge was seen as reducing the necessity for a Queensferry crossing.

A second Kincardine Bridge was given government go ahead in 1998 and work began on the new link roads in 2003. Costing an estimated ninety million pounds, the bridge is due for completion in 2008.

A new bridge at Queensferry is likely to cost somewhere in the region of four hundred million. If it does go ahead, it will be welcomed by the thousands of daily commuters, by transport and trade industries, and tourist and heritage organisations.

What is unlikely is that it will be greeted with the acclaim given to the 1964 Forth Road Bridge, which was such a splendid achievement.

Perhaps not the eighth wonder of the world that its neighbour was proclaimed, but a monument to Scottish ingenuity, skill and craftsmanship, and a source of continuing national pride.

Mary Fotheringham is one of the few females who have been on top of the main tower of the bridge.
Her father had a newsagent shop in Dunfermline and was friendly with the chief engineer, who organised the trip.
Mary, who was fifteen, and going through a series of operations at the time, had her leg in plaster when she made her memorable journey

Mary's view from the tower

FACTS AND FIGURES – 1964

The Forth Road Bridge is the largest suspension bridge in Europe, and, with the approach viaducts, is a little over one and a half miles long.

The central span is 3,300 feet between its two main towers. The side spans, which carry the deck to the side towers, are each 1,340 ft. long, and are flanked by approach viaducts.

At the side towers the supporting cables turn downwards towards the anchorages which are, essentially, massive wedges built by tunnelling into the rock. The cables are 2 ft. in diameter.

The main towers extend 512 ft. above mean river level and the sag of the cables between the towers is approximately 300 ft.

Under the deck of the main span there is headroom of 150 ft. close beside the piers, and this headroom increases to 163 ft. at mid-span.

The above dimensions of span, sag, tower height and shipping clearance give the bridge its basic sense of fitness for purpose, and result in a structure of slenderness and elegance combined with strength.

The dual 24 ft. wide roadways on the bridge were designed to carry the heaviest loading permitted on any roads in the world at the time, including vehicles weighing up to 180 tons. In addition to the two roadways there are two nine foot wide cycle tracks and two six foot wide footpaths.

Some 39,000 tons of steel and 150,000 cubic yards of concrete were used in the bridge construction.

Approach roads to the bridge include four and a half miles of dual carriageway on the southern side and three and a half miles dual carriageway on the northern side. Minor access roads extend for eight miles and there are twenty four minor bridges.

The total cost of The Forth Road Bridge is £19,500,000. The cost of The Forth Road Bridge project is met by the Government and constituent authorities in the area.

The Local Authorities, namely Edinburgh Corporation, Fife County Council, West Lothian County Council, Midlothian County Council, Dunfermline Town Council and Kirkcaldy Town Council contributed the total sum of £500,000.

The grant by the Secretary of State for Scotland amounted to £4,650,000. The balance of the sum required was borrowed from the Government.

The amount of the loan was £14,350,000.

The loan repayment, and running expenses to be met by toll charges each year was approximately £1,000,000.

The consulting engineers for The Forth Road Bridge project were Mott, Hay & Anderson, London and Edinburgh; Freeman, Fox & Partners, London, were associated with them for the main bridge and main approach viaducts.

The architect was the late Sir Giles Gilbert Scott, London. The principal contractors were:

Main bridge substructure – John Howard & Co., Ltd., London.

Superstructure – The A.C.D. Bridge Co., London, a partnership formed by Sir William Arrol & Co., Ltd., the Cleveland Bridge and Engineering Co. Ltd., and Dorman Long (Bridge & Engineering) Ltd.

Main approach viaducts – Reed & Malik, Ltd., Salisbury.

Northern approach roads – Whatlings Ltd., Glasgow.

Southern approach roads – A. M. Carmichael Ltd., Edinburgh.

The Authority for the whole project was the Forth Road Bridge Joint Board.

The approach roads begin to take shape

BIBLIOGRAPHY

The Forth Road Bridge, The Official Story – The Forth Road Joint Board
Silver Highway, The Story of the Forth Road Bridge – Sheila Mackay (Editor) – Moubray House Press
One Hundred Years of The Forth Bridge –Ed. Roland (editor) – Thomas Telford, London 1990
Crossing The Forth – Hugh Douglas. Robert Hale Ltd 1964
Passage of Time – Peter & Carol Dean. Peter & Carol Dean, 1981
Proceedings of the Institution of Civil Engineers – volume 32, November 1965

Dunfermline Press 1923 – 2003
The Scotsman – various dates
The Edinburgh Evening News – various dates
The Sunday Post – various dates
The People's Journal – various dates
The Scottish Daily Express – various dates
The Scottish Daily Mail – various dates

PICTURE ACKNOWLEDGEMENT

The Morris Allan Archive – frontispiece, 3, 5, 9, 11, 14, 17, 20, 21, 23, 26, 28 right, 30, 45, 46, 47, 48, 49, 50, 51, 52, 54, 58, 59, 63, 65, 66, 73, 78, 79, 83, 88, 89, 91, 94, 102, 103, 107 lower
Pictures by Morris Allan on pp 88, 89 by kind permission of Penny Girdler

The Forth Bridge Archives – 16, 18, 19, 22, 24, 25, 27, 28 left, 29, 32, 34, 36, 37, 39, 40, 41, 42, 43, 44, 57, 60, 61, 62, 64, 80, 81, 86, 93, 96, 98, 107 upper
Fife Constabulary – 68, 69, 71,
Madge Stobbie – 77
Campbell Morris – 84, 85, 87
Talisman Films – 53, 55, 56, 96, 98, 99, 106 lower
Mary Fotheringham – 100
The Proceedings of the Institution of Civil Engineers -Diagrams 104, 105
Penny Girdler – 106 upper
Mr & Mrs Alan Oliver – 106 lower

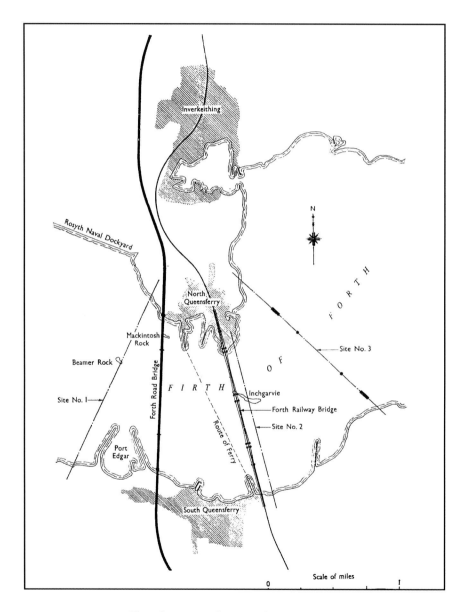

Plan of previous schemes and present bridges

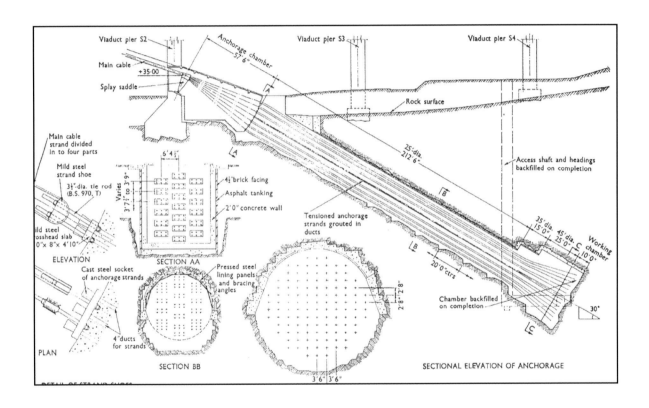

Plan of south anchorage chamber

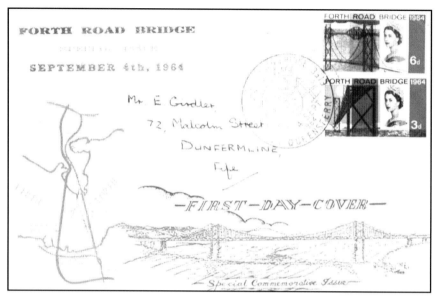

Two commemorative first day covers

ABOUT THE AUTHOR

Lillian King is a graduate of Edinburgh University. Most of her career has been in Adult Education and she is now a part time tutor with the WEA. Her particular interests are railways, mining and women's history. She has edited several anthologies of poetry and had articles in a variety of publications including The Scotsman, The Scots Magazine and The Times Educational Supplement.

Previous books include
A Railway Childhood
The Last Station
Thornton Railway Days
Famous Women of Fife
Sair, Sair Wark, Women and Mining in Scotland
That's Entertainment, 100 Years of Dunfermline Opera House